Key Facts Reference Library

KU-242-173

G.C.E. O-Level

TRADITIONAL AND MODERN
MATHEMATICS

by Krysia Ahmad, M.A.

key facts

Published by Intercontinental Book Productions
in conjunction with Seymour Press Ltd.
Distributed by Seymour Press Ltd.,
334 Brixton Road, London, SW9 7AG

Published 1978 by Intercontinental Book Productions, Berkshire House, Queen Street, Maidenhead, Berks. SL6 1NF in conjunction with Seymour Press Ltd.

1st edition, 1st impression 8.78.1
Copyright © 1978 Intercontinental Book Productions
Made and printed in England by C. Nicholls & Company Ltd.
ISBN 0 85047 9193

KRYSIA AHMAD obtained her B.A. honours degree in the natural sciences, and later her M.A. degree, from the University of Cambridge. While at Cambridge she taught chemistry, physics and mathematics on a private tutorial basis. She has considerable experience of publishing, having edited many research journals and scientific publications. She has been involved in the Key Facts series in a scientific advisory capacity and is now a freelance writer and editor.

Reference Library

BIOLOGY, R. Whitaker, B.Sc. and
J. M. Kelly, B.Sc.

CHEMISTRY, K. Ahmad, M.A.

PHYSICS, K. Ahmad, M.A.

Contents

Introduction

This book is intended primarily for students offering modern mathematics at GCE O level, but it will also provide useful background material for the many people who require a working knowledge of mathematics to O level standard.

The book is designed to serve both as a quick and easy reference book and as an aid to revision. The contents cover all the main topics and many of the optional ones listed by the various examining boards.

The subject material is divided into topics, each topic consisting of a list of statements, definitions and formulae. The entries are arranged in a logical subject order and not in alphabetical order. Each entry begins with a title in bold typescript placed at the left hand side of the page, a word or words appearing in bold in the body of the entry denote an important term or concept. Each entry has been written in an easy to understand form with necessary details and explanations being given. The book is well illustrated to aid understanding of the material. A list of mathematical symbols is given on page 7.

Metric units have been used throughout although occasionally a non-metric unit which is still widely used has been given. A list of metric units and symbols is given on page 92.

Students often experience difficulty in extracting and appreciating the essential elements of a concept. It is hoped that this book, in presenting the material in a concise yet simple form will help the student to not only increase his knowledge of basic facts or to refresh his memory but also to increase his understanding of the core or essence of the subject.

Mathematical symbols

$+$ plus; the sign of addition, also may mean positive.

$-$ minus; the sign of subtraction, also may mean negative.

$\pm$ plus or minus, as the case may be.

$\times$ sign of multiplication; multiplied by or into.

$\div$ sign of division; divided by.

$\sim$ the difference between two quantities leaving it doubtful which is the greater.

$=$ sign of equality; equals; is equal or equivalent to.

$\neq$ is not equal to.

$\simeq$ is approximately equal to.

$>$ is greater than e.g. $a > b$ means a is greater than b.

$\geqslant$ is greater than or equal to.

$<$ is less than e.g. $a < b$ means a is less than b.

$\leqslant$ is less than or equal to.

$\propto$ is proportional to, varies as e.g. $a \propto b$ says a is proportional to b.

$:$ is to, e.g. $a:b$ says a is to b.

$\Rightarrow$ implies e.g. $x = 3 \Rightarrow y = 4$ says if $x = 3$ then $y = 4$.

$\Leftarrow$ is implied by e.g. $x = 1 \Leftarrow y = 4$ says $x = 1$ if $y = 4$.

$\Leftrightarrow$ implies and vice versa e.g. $x = 1 \Leftrightarrow y = 4$ says if $x = 1$ then $y = 4$ and vice versa.

∞ infinity, infinitely great.

$\sqrt{}, \sqrt{}$ square root sign e.g. $\sqrt{4} = 2$.

$\sqrt[3]{}$ cube root sign e.g. $\sqrt[3]{8} = 2$.

$( ), \{ \}, [ ]$ indicates that the enclosed quantities are to be treated together as forming a single term.

$\angle$ angle e.g. $\angle ABC$ is angle ABC.

$\llcorner$ right angle e.g. $\llcorner ABC$ says the right angle ABC.

$\perp$ the perpendicular, perpendicular to e.g. $AB \perp CD$ says AB is perpendicular to CD.

$\parallel$ parallel, parallel to e.g. $AB \parallel CD$ says AB is parallel to CD.

$\triangle$ triangle e.g. $\triangle ABC$ is triangle ABC.

π ratio of circumference of a circle to its diameter $= 3 \cdot 142$ correct to 3 decimal places.

$^\circ$ degree or degrees e.g. $32°C$ (temperature), $360°$ (circular measure).

$'$ minutes in circular measure e.g. $5°15'$

$''$ seconds in circular measure e.g. $5°3'6''$

Sets

Much more importance is now being attached to Set Theory mainly because of the unifying influence it has on mathematics as a whole. Set Theory is of fundamental importance in the theory of probability and now also plays a significant role in the fields of switching circuits and electronic computers.

Language

A set is a general name for any collection of distinct elements. The elements of a set may be defined either by enumerating them or by stating a rule. A pair of braces, { }, is the symbol used for enclosing the elements of a set; a set is usually denoted by a capital letter.

Examples of sets:

$A = \{1, 3, 5, 7\}$ This is the set of the first four odd integers
$B = \{x : x$ is an odd integer, $0 < x < 8\}$ This is the same set as A
$C = \{$The solutions of the equation $x^2 - x - 6 = 0\}$
$D = \{$Publishers of Great Britain$\}$

The elements of a set may be written in any order. For example, $\{a, e, i, o, u\}$ is the same set as $\{e, o, i, a, u\}$. The elements of a set are distinct so that for example the elements of the set of letters contained in the word 'borrow' are $\{b, o, r, w\}$.

A subset If every element of one set, B, is a member of a second set, A, then B is a subset of A written $B \subset A$ e.g.

$$\{1, 3, 5\} \text{ is a subset of } \{1, 3, 5, 7, 9\}$$

$$\{\text{All isosceles triangles}\} \text{ is a subset of } \{\text{All triangles}\}$$

The universal set, $\mathscr{E}$, denotes all elements under consideration i.e. if each of the sets being considered is a subset of another set, then this set is the universal set e.g.

$\{\text{Integers}\}$ is a universal set of the subsets $A = \{1, 2, 3\}$ and $B = \{8, 9\}$

$$\{\text{Animals}\} \text{ is a universal set of the subset } \{\text{Mammals}\}$$

The null or empty set, { } or $\varnothing$, has no elements e.g.

$\{\text{Triangles with four sides}\}$
$\{\text{Animals with three legs}\}$

Equal sets Two sets A and B are equal, written $A = B$, if they have the same elements, irrespective of order e.g.

$$A = \{2, 4, 6\} \text{ and } B = \{6, 2, 4\} \text{ are equal sets}$$

$$C = \{a, i, o, u\} \text{ and } D = \{i, u, o, a\} \text{ are equal sets}$$

Equivalent sets Two sets A and B are equivalent, written $A \leftrightarrow B$, if to each element of set A there corresponds an element in set B and to each element of set B there corresponds an element in set A. The elements of the two sets are said to be in one-to-one correspondence.

For finite sets. Two finite sets are equivalent if they contain the same number of elements e.g.

If $A = \{1, 3, 5\}$ and $B = \{2, 4, 6\}$ then A and B are equivalent.

For infinite sets. The equivalence of two infinite sets is more difficult to determine. If there is a one-one correspondence between the elements in the two sets then they are equivalent.
e.g. {All odd integers} is equivalent to {All even integers} since there exists a one-to-one correspondence between the elements of the two sets defined by $y = x + 1$.

The complement of a set A, denoted A', is the set of the elements in $\mathscr{E}$ which are not in A e.g.

If $\mathscr{E} = \{a, e, i, o, u\}$ and $A = \{a, i, u\}$, then $A' = \{e, o\}$
If $\mathscr{E} = \{1, 3, 5, 7, 9\}$ and $A = \{3, 7, 9\}$, then $A' = \{1, 5\}$

Disjoint sets are sets which have no elements in common e.g.

If $A = \{1, 3, 5\}$ and $B = \{2, 4, 6\}$, then A and B are disjoint sets
If $X = \{\text{All circles}\}$ and $Y = \{\text{All triangles}\}$, then X and Y are disjoint sets.

A finite set is a set which has a finite number of elements e.g.

{Odd numbers from 1 to 19},
{Members of Parliament}

An infinite set is a set which contains an infinite number of elements. The elements of such a set cannot be enumerated e.g.

{All integers},
{All primes}

A continuous set If every point or number which lies between any two elements of a set is itself an element of the set, then the set is said to be continuous e.g.

{The points on an ellipse}

A discrete set If any point or number which lies between any two members of a set is not itself a member of the set, then the set is said to be discrete e.g.

{The integers} since all the fractions lying between any two integers are not themselves members of the set.

A closed set is one in which both elements of the set are defined e.g.

$$\{4 \leqslant x \leqslant 17\}, \quad \{1, 4, 9 \ldots n\}$$

An open set is one in which either both or one of the end elements is not defined e.g.

$\{4 \leqslant x < 17\}$ and $\{1, 4, 9 \ldots\}$ are open sets because the largest element is not defined.

The intersection of sets A and B, written $A \cap B$, is the set containing the elements common to both sets. $A \cap B$ reads either as 'A intersection B' or 'A cup B'.

Examples
If $A = \{2, 4, 6\}$ and $B = \{4, 5, 6\}$, then $A \cap B = \{4, 6\}$
If $C = \{$All circles$\}$ and $D = \{$All triangles$\}$, then $C \cap D = \varnothing$
If $X = \{$Squares$\}$ and $Y = \{$Parallelograms$\}$, $X \cap Y = \{$Squares$\}$

Points about intersection of sets
1. If $A \subset B$ (A is a subset of B) then $A \cap B = A$.
2. If A and B are disjoint, then $A \cap B = \varnothing$ (null set).
3. $A \cap A' = \varnothing$ (the intersection of A and its complement A' is the null set).
4. $A \cap A' = \varnothing$ and $A \cap A = A$.

The union of sets A and B, written $A \cup B$, is the set containing the elements in A or B or both. $A \cup B$ is read either as 'A union B' or 'A cup B'. If sets A and B have elements in common then these elements are only listed once in the union set.

Examples
If $A = \{$a, b, c, d$\}$ and $B = \{$c, d, e, f$\}$, then $A \cup B = \{$a, b, c, d, e, f$\}$
If $B = \{$All fair-haired girls$\}$ and $C = \{$All fair-haired boys$\}$ then $B \cup C = \{$All fair-haired girls and all fair-haired boys$\}$
If $A = \{2, 4, 6\}$, $B = \{6, 8\}$ and $C = \{7, 8, 9\}$, then $A \cup B \cup C = \{2, 4, 6, 7, 8, 9\}$

Points about union of sets
1. If $A \subset B$ (A is a subset of B), then $A \cup B = B$
2. $A \cup A' = \mathscr{E}$
3. $A \cup A = A$

Symbols

A = {**a, b, c, d**} ; A is the set of the first four letters of the alphabet.

n(A), is the number of elements in set A.

4 ∈ A, 4 is an element or member of set A.

8 ∉ B, 8 is not an element or member of set B.

A ⊂ B, A is a subset of B, means that all the elements of set A are also the elements of set B.

B ⊃ A, B includes A, means that all the elements of set A are also the elements of set B. (This is another way of writing $A \subset B$.)

$\mathscr{E}$, denotes the universal set, which is the set of elements under consideration.

∅ or { }, called the empty or null set, is the set which has no elements.

A = B, A and B are equal sets, occurs when the two sets have the same elements irrespective of order.

A ↔ B, A is equivalent to B, occurs when the two sets have the same number of elements.

A′, the complement of A, is the set of elements in $\mathscr{E}$ but not in A.

A ∩ B, A cup B or A intersection B, means the set of the elements which are in both A and B.

A ∪ B, A cup B or A union B, means the set of the elements which are either in A or B or both.

Venn diagrams

Venn diagrams are diagrams which help to clarify set manipulation. A rectangle is usually chosen to represent the universal set and circles to represent the subsets.

Venn diagrams are often used to solve problems involving numbers in sets (an example of which is given on pages 12–13). A number inside or on the boundary of the circles represents the number of the set. The areas of the circles are not made proportional to the number of the set.

The circles representing the subsets are drawn so as to have the greatest possible number of intersections unless information is supplied which makes this untrue.

Inclusion, $A \subset B$, may be represented as in Figure 1a

Disjoint sets may be represented as in Figure 1b

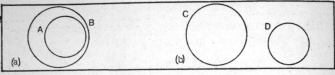

Figure 1a

Figure 1b

Complement The complement of set A, A' is represented by the shaded area in Figure 1c.

Union and Intersection The darker shaded area represents $A \cap B$, the lighter shaded area $A \cup B$.

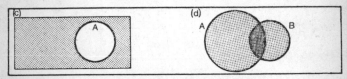

Figure 1c

Figure 1d

Solution of a set problem using Venn diagrams

$\mathscr{E}$ = pupils
Suppose $n(\mathscr{E}) = 140$ pupils
Let $B = \{$Pupils who play badminton$\}$ and $n(B) = 80$
Let $T = \{$Pupils who play tennis$\}$
and $n(T) = 90$
$B \cap T = \{$Pupils who play both badminton and tennis$\}$
where $n(B \cap T) = 40$

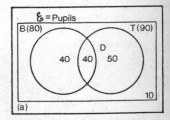

Shaded areas represent

$B \cap T$: $\{$Pupils who play both badminton and tennis$\}$
$n(B \cap T) = 40$

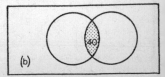

12

$B \cup T$: {Pupils who play badminton or tennis or both}

$n(B \cup T) = 130$

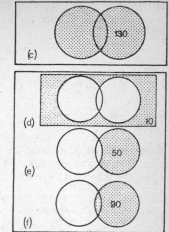

$(B \cup T)'$: Pupils who do not play badminton or tennis

$n(B \cup T)' = 10$

$T \cap B'$ {Pupils who play tennis and not badminton}

$n(T \cap B') = 50$

T: {Pupils who play tennis}

$n(T) = 90$

Figure 2

Laws of Sets

The commutative law

$$A \cup B = B \cup A$$

and

$$A \cap B = B \cap A$$

since intersection and union are commutative processes, i.e. it does not matter which set is written first when finding a union or intersection of two sets.

The associative law

for union $\quad A \cup (B \cup C) = (A \cup B) \cup C = A \cup B \cup C$

for intersection $A \cap (B \cap C) = (A \cap B) \cap C = A \cap B \cap C$

Figure 3 shows that the intersection of sets is associative and Figure 4 shows that the union of sets is associative.

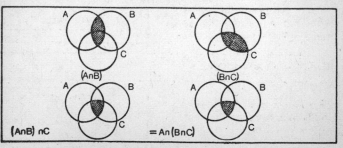

Figure 3. To show that the intersection of sets is associative

13

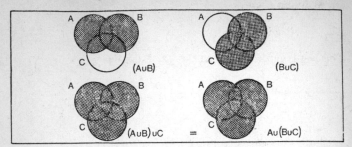

Figure 4. To show that the union of sets is associative

The distributive law

for intersection over union $A \cap (B \cup C) = (A \cap B) \cup (A \cap C)$
for union over intersection $A \cup (B \cap C) = (A \cup B) \cap (A \cup C)$
Figure 5 shows that intersection is distributive over union and Figure
6 that union is distributive over intersection.

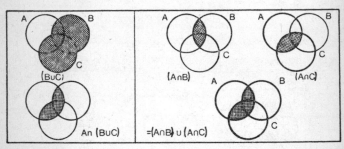

Figure 5. To show that intersection is distributive over union

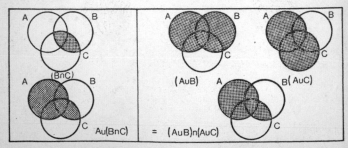

Figure 6. To show that union is distributive over intersection

de Morgan's laws

$$(A \cap B)' = A' \cup B'$$

and

$$(A \cup B)' = A' \cap B'$$

This law is verified by using the Venn diagram below.

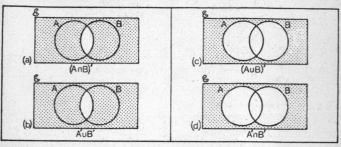

Figure 7. To verify de Morgan's laws

The laws of absorption

$$A \cap (A \cup B) = A$$

and

$$A \cup (A \cap B) = A$$

This law is verified by using the Venn diagram below.

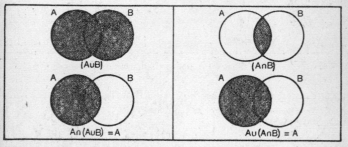

Figure 8. To verify the laws of absorption

Numbers and Number Systems

Numbers

Whole numbers are the counting numbers including zero. They are always positive. Whole numbers are a subset of the set of integers.

Examples: 0, 1, 2, 3, 4.

Natural numbers are whole numbers excluding zero. Natural numbers are therefore also a subset of the set of integers.

Integers are whole numbers but they also include negative numbers and zero.

Examples: -43, -2, 0, 5, 176

Prime numbers are whole numbers, excluding 1, which have no factors except 1 and themselves.
The first five prime numbers are 2, 3, 5, 7, 11

Rational numbers are numbers which can be expressed as a fraction or a ratio i.e. they are of the form m/n where m and n are integers, but n cannot be zero.

Examples: $\frac{2}{3}$, $\frac{1}{2}$, $\frac{5}{1}$, $\frac{10}{2}$, $0 \cdot 74$ and all recurring decimals such as $0 \cdot \dot{3}$ $(\frac{1}{3})$, $0 \cdot 142857$ $(\frac{1}{7})$

Irrational numbers are numbers which cannot be expressed as a fraction or ratio of integers.
Examples: Surds (such as $\sqrt{2}$, $\sqrt{3}$, $\sqrt{5}$, $\sqrt{6}$), π.

No matter to how many decimal places these numbers are calculated the decimal never ends which means that the number cannot be expressed exactly.

Real numbers are all the numbers on the number line. Integers, whole numbers, natural numbers, rational and irrational numbers, and prime numbers are all real numbers.

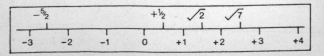

16

Number systems in different bases

Denary or decimal system (Base 10) This system has ten digits 0, 1, 2, 3, 4, 5, 6, 7, 8 and 9. The column headings are the powers of ten:

$$\ldots 10000 \quad 1000 \quad 100 \quad 10 \quad 1 \quad \tfrac{1}{10} \quad \tfrac{1}{100} \ldots$$

or

$$10^4 \quad 10^3 \quad 10^2 \quad 10^1 \quad 10^0 \quad 10^{-1} \quad 10^{-2}$$

For example the denary number

7621_{10} means 1 unit (10^0) + 2 tens (10^1) + 6 hundreds (10^2) + 7 thousands (10^3)

Binary system (Base 2) This system has two digits 0 and 1. It has assumed great importance since the introduction of computers; these consist of large numbers of circuits in which the current can either be switched off or on. They therefore need a number base with only two digits i.e. 0 for switched off and 1 for switched on. The column headings in the binary system are powers of two:

$$\ldots 10000 \quad 1000 \quad 100 \quad 10 \quad 1 \quad \tfrac{1}{10} \quad \tfrac{1}{100} \quad \text{in base 2}$$

or

$$16 \quad 8 \quad 4 \quad 2 \quad 1 \quad \tfrac{1}{2} \quad \tfrac{1}{4} \quad \text{in base 10}$$

or

$$2^4 \quad 2^3 \quad 2^2 \quad 2^1 \quad 2^0 \quad 2^{-1} \quad 2^{-2} \quad \text{in base 10}$$

For example the binary number:
111011_2 means 1 unit (2^0) + 1 two (2^1) + 0 fours (2^2) + 1 eight (2^3) + 1 sixteen (2^4) + 1 thirty two (2^5)
$$= 59_{10} \text{ in denary}$$

Octal system (Base 8) This system has eight digits 0, 1, 2, 3, 4, 5, 6 and 7. The column headings are powers of eight:

$$\ldots 1000 \quad 100 \quad 10 \quad 1 \quad \tfrac{1}{10} \quad \tfrac{1}{100} \quad \text{in base 8}$$

or

$$512 \quad 64 \quad 8 \quad 1 \quad \tfrac{1}{8} \quad \tfrac{1}{64} \quad \text{in base 10}$$

or

$$8^3 \quad 8^2 \quad 8^1 \quad 8^0 \quad 8^{-1} \quad 8^{-2} \quad \text{in base 10}$$

For example the octal number:
243_8 means 3 units (8^0) + 4 eights (8^1) + 2 sixty-fours (8^2)
$$= 163_{10} \text{ in denary}$$

17

The first ten denary numbers written as binary and octal numbers

Denary Base 10 1	Binary Base 8 4 2 1	Octal Base 8 1
1	1	1
2	1 0	2
3	1 1	3
4	1 0 0	4
5	1 0 1	5
6	1 1 0	6
7	1 1 1	7
8	1 0 0 0	1 0
9	1 0 0 1	1 1
1 0	1 0 1 0	1 2

Converting binary or octal to denary

Multiply each digit in the number by the appropriate power of two (for binary number) or eight (for octal number) and add. e.g.

(i) To convert 10101_2 from binary to denary:

Multiplying from the right

$10101_2 = 1 \times 2^0 + 0 \times 2^1 + 1 \times 2^2 + 0 \times 2^3 + 1 \times 2^4$
$= 1 + 4 + 16 = 21_{10}$

(ii) To convert 7204 from octal to denary:

$7204_8 = 4 \times 8^0 + 0 \times 8^1 + 2 \times 8^2 + 7 \times 8^3$
$= 4 + 128 + 3584 = 3716_{10}$

Converting denary to binary or octal

Repeatedly divide the denary number by two (for binary number) or eight (for octal number) recording the remainders and putting zero where there is no remainder. From the bottom to the top gives the number from left to right. Examples:

(i) To convert 29 to binary

```
2 | 29
2 | 14   r1
2 |  7   r0
2 |  3   r1
2 |  1   r1
2 |  3   r1
2 |  1   r1
  |  0   r1
```

$29_{10} = 11101_2$

(ii) To convert 123 to octal

```
8 | 123
8 |  15   r3
8 |   1   r7
  |   0   r1
```

$123_{10} = 173_8$

Converting binary to octal

For example to convert 11010111_2 to octal. Procedure:

1. Split the binary number into triples from the right:

$$11_2 \quad 010_2 \quad 111_2$$

2. Write down the octal equivalent of each triple:

$$11 \quad 010 \quad 111$$

$$3_8 \quad 2_8 \quad 7_8$$

3. This is the required number i.e. $11010111_2 = 327_8$

Converting octal to binary

For example to convert 3764_8 to binary. Procedure:

1. For each digit write down the equivalent binary triple:

$$3 \quad 7 \quad 6 \quad 4$$
$$011_2 \quad 111_2 \quad 110_2 \quad 100_2$$

2. Ignoring the initial zero this gives the binary number:

$$3764_8 = 11111110100_2$$

Binary addition

Addition table	*Examples:*	
$0 + 0 = 0$	(i) $\quad 1011$	(ii) $\quad 11010$
$0 + 1 = 1$	$\quad +1101$	$\quad +1111$
$1 + 0 = 1$		
$1 + 1 = 10$	$\quad 11000$	$\quad 101001$
$1 + 1 + 1 = 11$		

(i) In the units column $1 + 1 = 10$, put down 0 and carry 1: in the 2's column $1 + 0 + 1 = 10$, put down 0 and carry 1; in the 4's column $0 + 1 + 1 = 10$, put down zero and carry 1; in the 8's column $1 + 1 + 1 = 11$.

Binary subtraction

Subtraction table	*Examples:*	11110
$0 - 0 = 0$	(i) $\quad 10110$	(ii) $\quad 10000$
$1 - 0 = 1$	$\quad -1011$	$\quad -1011$
$1 - 1 = 0$		
$10 - 1 = 1$	$\quad 1011$	$\quad 101$

(i) In the units column, $0 - 1$ is not possible, so we borrow 1 from the 2's column. Then $10 - 1 = 1$. The top of the 2's column now equals zero, and since $0 - 1$ is not possible we borrow 1 from the 4's column. Then $10 - 1 = 1$. In the 4's column, $0 - 0 = 0$. To subtract the 8's column we borrow 1 from the 16's column so $10 - 1 = 1$.

(ii) In the case where the top line contains a number of 0's the number is written out in an extended form i.e. $10000 = 16 = 8 + 4 + 2 + 2$ which in binary is written above the 10000 (Note 10 in the last column represents 2). 1011 is subtracted from this line.

Binary multiplication

Multiplication table

	Examples:		
$0 \times 0 = 0$	(i)	(ii)	

```
0 × 0 = 0          (i)    1101        (ii)    1101
1 × 0 = 0               ×  11               × 111
0 × 1 = 0              ─────              ─────
1 × 1 = 1               1101               1101
                      11010              11010
                     ──────            110100
                     100111            ──────
                                      1011011
```

Multiplication is straight forward. Proceed as for multiplication in denary except that one is working in base 2 not base 10.

Binary division

To evaluate $100010 \div 101$ treat as long division. If 101 goes in to a binary number it goes once, write 1; if it does not go write 0. $100010 \div 101 =$ 110 remainder 100

```
        110 remainder 100
   101 ) 100010
         111
         101
         ───
         100
```

Bicimals or binary fractions are the fractional parts of binary numbers. The headings appear thus:

Decimal							Bicimal							
... 100	10	1	$\frac{1}{10}$	$\frac{1}{100}$	$\frac{1}{1000}$	...	... 8	4	2	1	$\frac{1}{2}$	$\frac{1}{4}$	$\frac{1}{8}$	$\frac{1}{16}$ ...

To convert bicimals to decimals

For example, to convert $1001 \cdot 1101_2$ to decimal, place the digits under the correct bicimal heading and add:

$$8 \quad 4 \quad 2 \quad 1 \qquad \tfrac{1}{2} \quad \tfrac{1}{4} \quad \tfrac{1}{8} \quad \tfrac{1}{16}$$
$$1 \quad 0 \quad 0 \quad 1 \cdot 1 \quad 1 \quad 0 \quad 1$$

which gives $8 + 1 \cdot \frac{1}{2} + \frac{1}{4} + \frac{1}{16}$

This gives $9 + 0.5 + 0.250 + 0.0625 = 9.8125$

To convert decimals to bicimals Procedure:

1. Split the fractions into bicimals
2. Write the binary equivalent for each integer and fraction

(i) When the decimal fraction can be split into bicimals

For example, to convert $5\frac{7}{16}$ to bicimals is straight forward since it can be split into

$$5\tfrac{7}{16} = 5 + \tfrac{1}{4} + \tfrac{1}{8} + \tfrac{1}{16} = 101 \cdot 0111_2$$

(ii) When the decimal fraction cannot be split into bicimals. Procedure:

1. Change the fraction to binary
2. Perform binary division

To convert $7\frac{3}{5}$ to bicimals

$$\frac{3}{5} = \frac{11}{101} \quad 101 \overline{\smash{\big)}\begin{array}{l} 0{\cdot}10011 \\ 11{\cdot}00000 \end{array}}$$

$$\begin{array}{r} 101 \\ \hline 1000 \\ 101 \\ \hline 110 \end{array}$$

$7\frac{3}{5} = 111{\cdot}1001$ to four bicimal places.

Arithmetic modulo 5

In arithmetic modulo 5 it is assumed that the only numbers are the digits 0, 1, 2, 3, 4. For purposes of calculating in modulo 5 the digits are placed on a clock face as in figure 9. For calculations in arithmetic n where n is a positive integer the digits from 0 to $n - 1$ would be placed equally round the face of a clock.

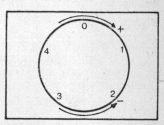

Figure 9

Addition and subtraction in modulo 5

To add $4 + 2$ point the hand of the clock at zero. Move it four units clockwise then 2 units clockwise. The hand now points at 1. Hence in modulo 5, $4 + 2 = 1$. To subtract $7 - 2$, point the hand of the clock at zero. Move it 7 units clockwise then two units anticlockwise. The hand now points at zero. Hence in modulo 5, $7 - 2 = 0$.

Properties of addition table for modulo 5

1. The commutative law holds i.e.
$$a + b = b + a$$
2. The associative law holds i.e.
$$a + (b + c) = (a + b) + c$$
3. In any row or column the numbers with which we started occur and none is repeated.
4. The set contains an identity element which is zero i.e. for any element a, then $0 + a = a + 0 = a$.

+	0	1	2	3	4
0	0	1	2	3	4
1	1	2	3	4	0
2	2	3	4	0	1
3	3	4	0	1	2
4	4	0	1	2	3

5. The table is closed i.e. only the numbers we started with occur.
6. Subtraction is possible. To evaluate $2 - 4$ we go to the bottom row which is labelled 4 and then move along this row until we come to 2. The heading in this column is 3. Hence in modulo 5, $2 - 4 = 3$.

Multiplication in modulo 5

To multiply 3 × 4, point the hand at zero and move it 3 units clockwise. Repeat this three more times. The hand now points at 2. Therefore 3 × 4 = 2.

Properties of the multiplication table for modulo 5

1. The commutative law holds i.e.
$$ab = ba$$
2. The associative law holds i.e.
$$a(bc) = (ab)c$$
3. In any row or column, all the numbers we started with will occur and none is repeated.
4. The set contains the identity element which is 1 i.e.
$1 \times a = a \times 1 = a$ for any number a

×	1	2	3	4
1	1	2	3	4
2	2	4	1	3
3	3	1	4	2
4	4	3	2	1

5. The table is closed i.e. only the numbers we started with will occur.
6. Division is possible. For example, to evaluate 2 ÷ 3 we go to the row labelled 3, move along this row until we reach 2. The heading in this column is 4. Hence in modulo 5, 2 ÷ 3 = 4.

Binary operations

A binary operation is an operation carried out on any two members of a set S. The symbol used is ∗, where ∗ can be +, −, ×, ÷, ( ), etc. If the results are tabulated we have an operation table.

Closure A set S is closed under operation if, for all elements a and b in S, $a * b$ is also in S i.e. if all the elements of the operation table ∈ S. For example, consider the set of positive integers 1 = (0, 1, 2, 3 ...) this set is closed under the operations addition and multiplication. It is not closed under the operation subtraction, which may produce negative integers or under the operation division which may produce fractions.

The identity element, *I*, of a set is the number which, when combined with any number of the set under a given operation leaves the value of the member unaltered i.e. $a * I = I * a = a$. For example, the identity element for addition is zero since 3 + 0 = 3; the identity element for multiplication is 1 since 3 × 1 = 3.

The inverse element, A^{-1}, of a member *A* under a given operation is that member which when combined with the member produces the identity element i.e. $a \times A^{-1} = A^{-1} \times a = I$. For example, for addition −4 is the inverse of +4, because (4) + (−4) = 0 and 0 is the identity element for addition.

The associative law The operation $*$ is associative if, for every element of the set under operation $(a*b)*c = a*(b*c)$. For example, addition is associative since $(4 + 3) + 2 = 4 + (3 + 2)$.

Groups If a set S under an operation $*$ is
1. closed
2. has an identity element which is a member of S
3. each term has an inverse which is also an element of S
4. is associative
then the set S forms a group under $*$.
For example modulo 5 forms a group under addition. It does not form a group under multiplication since the inverses of the elements do not belong to S.

Commutative or Abelian groups If in addition to the above properties for a group the operation is commutative i.e. $a*b = b*a$, then the group is called commutative or Abelian.

Isomorphic groups Two groups are isomorphic if they have the same structure or form. When the operation tables are drawn up corresponding results appear.

Functions

A relation is a connection between the elements of two sets. For example, in the statements AB is parallel to CD, 16 is the square of 4, the words 'is parallel to', 'is the square of' are relations between the elements of two sets.

A mapping is the linking of the elements of one set, A, with their images in another set, B. If the elements of A are mapped on to those of B, A is called the **domain** and B the **range**.

A function is a relation in which each element of the domain is mapped on to one and only one element of the range. The function has *one-to-one correspondence* if every point of A is mapped on to a unique element of B and no two points of A are mapped on to the same element of B.

Symbol for a function

There are two equivalent ways of representing functions:

$$f : x \rightarrow x^3 \qquad \text{and} \qquad f(x) = x^3$$

Both mean f is the function which maps x on to x^3.

A mapping diagram In a mapping diagram the elements of the domain and range are shown on two vertical number scales. A straight line connects elements of the domain and range. For example, figure 10(a) shows the mapping diagram of the function $f : x \rightarrow 2x + 1$ for the domain $\{-2, -1, 0, 1, 2\}$. The range is $\{-3, -1, 1, 3, 5\}$.

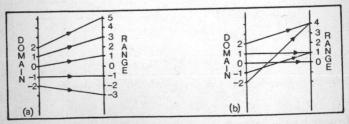

Figure 10. Mapping diagram

Figure 10(b) shows the mapping diagram of the function $f : x \rightarrow x^2$ for the domain $\{-2, -1, 0, 1, 2\}$. The range is $\{4, 1, 0, 1, 4\}$.

The compound function $fg(x)$ means g followed by f. For example, if $f:x \to x + 1$ and $g:x \to 2x^2$ then $fg(x) = 2x^2 + 1$. Usually $fg \neq gf$.

The inverse function of f, f^{-1}, maps the range on to the domain. The inverse of addition is subtraction, of multiplication is division, of squaring is square rooting and vice versa.

For example, if $f:x \to x + 4$ then $f^{-1}:x \to x - 4$
if $f:x \to x \times 3$ then $f^{-1}:x \to x \div 3$
if $f:x \to x^2$ then $f^{-1}:x \to +\sqrt{x}$

The inverse of a complex function is best determined using a flow diagram. Note the following inverses:

if $f:x \to x$ then $f^{-1}:x \to x$
if $f:x \to 1/x$ then $f^{-1}:x \to 1/x$
if $f:x \to 5 - x$ then $f^{-1}:x \to 5 - x$

A flow diagram is used to plan the correct sequence of events. They can be used to determine inverse functions of a more complex kind or to rearrange formulae.

Determination of inverse functions using flow diagrams

If $f:x \to \frac{1}{3}(2x + 1)$ find the inverse.

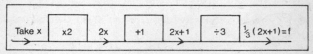

To find f^{-1} take the inverse of every process, from right to left.

If $f = \frac{1}{3}(2x + 1)$, $f^{-1} = \frac{1}{2}(3x - 1)$

Variation

Direct proportion If y varies directly as x, then

$$y \propto x \quad \text{or} \quad y = kx \quad \text{where } k \text{ is a constant}$$

Inverse proportion If y varies inversely as x, then

$$y \propto \frac{1}{x} \quad \text{or} \quad xy = k \quad \text{where } k \text{ is a constant}$$

Rates of change

Distance/time graphs

Figure 11 shows the distance (in km) travelled by a car against time (in hours).

The gradient of the graph at any point

$$= \frac{\text{distance}}{\text{time}}$$

$= \text{speed}$

A straight line such as OA and BC shows that the car is travelling with uniform speed over that time interval. A horizontal line such as AB shows that the car is stationary during that time interval.

Average speed for the whole journey $= \dfrac{\text{total distance}}{\text{total time}}$

$$= \frac{160}{7}$$

$= 22 \cdot 9 \, \text{km/hr}$

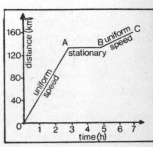

Figure 11. Distance/time graph

Velocity/time graphs

Figure 12 shows the velocity (in m/s) of an object against time (in seconds).

The gradient of the graph $= \dfrac{\text{velocity}}{\text{time}} = $ acceleration at any point.

A straight line sloping upward such as OA indicates uniform acceleration.

A straight line sloping downward such as BC indicates uniform retardation.

A horizontal line such as AB indicates zero acceleration and hence the object must be travelling with uniform velocity.

Area under velocity/time graph
= distance travelled
$= \frac{1}{2} AD \cdot OD + DE \cdot AD + \frac{1}{2} BE \cdot EC$
$= \frac{1}{2} \times 12 \times 2 + 12 \times 3 + \frac{1}{2} \times 12 \times 2$
$= 12 + 36 + 12 = 60$ units
distance travelled $= 60 \, \text{m}$

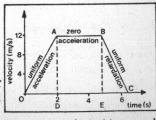

Figure 12. Velocity/time graph

26

Inequalities

An inequality or ordering states that one quantity is greater than or less than another.

The signs of the inequalities are:

$>$ greater than
$<$ less than
$\geqslant$ greater than or equal to
$\leqslant$ less than or equal to

Rules of inequalities

The rules for addition, subtraction, multiplication and division which keep the inequality true, follow.

We can:

1. Add the same number to both sides.
2. Subtract the same number from both sides.
3. Multiply or divide both sides by the same positive number.
4. When multiplying or dividing by a negative number the inequality sign must be reversed.

For example, consider the statement $7 > 3$ and the inequality $4x + 2 > 5$.

Adding 2	$9 > 5$	$4x + 4 > 7$
Subtracting 3	$4 > 0$	$4x - 1 > 2$
Multiplying by 2	$14 > 6$	$8x + 4 > 10$
Dividing by -1	$-7 < -3$	$-4x - 2 < -5$

An inequation is an inequality which contains one or more unknown variables e.g. $4x + 3 > 6$; $2x^2 + 1 \geqslant 3x + 27$. Inequations can be solved in much the same ways as equations.

The solution set of an inequation is the range of values which satisfy the inequation.

Solution of inequations

Linear inequations (i) In one unknown can be solved by applying the rules of inequalities. For example:

To solve $\quad 5x - 4 > 2x + 5$
Subtract $2x$ from both sides $\quad 3x - 4 > 5$
Add 4 to both sides $\quad 3x > 9$
Divide both sides by 3 $\quad \Leftrightarrow x > 3 \quad$ which is the solution set.

27

(ii) In 2 unknowns these can be solved graphically, e.g.

To solve $y > x + 2$

Draw the graph of $y = x + 2$ Choose a convenient point, usually the origin side of the line and insert the coordinates into the equation to see which side of the line the inequation applies. Shade out the other side. All the points (x, y) on the left side of the line satisfy the inequation.

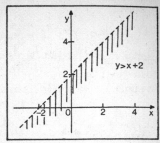

Figure 13

Quadratic inequations

These are best solved either by using the number line or by drawing a graph. For example:

1. To solve $x^2 \geqslant 4$

Try values of x which will satisfy the inequation and mark the range of x on the number line. Shade the part of the number line which does not obey the inequation.

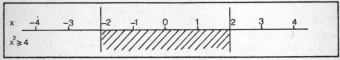

Figure 14

The solution set is $\{x : x \leqslant -2$ or $x \geqslant 2\}$

2. To solve $x^2 - 3x + 2 < 0$ Draw a stretch of the curve $x^2 - 3x + 2 = y$.

The function is less than zero for $1 < x < 2$ which is the solution set of the inequation.

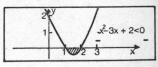

Figure 15

Simultaneous inequations

These can be solved either by applying the rules of inequalities or graphically.

Solution by rules

1. If the two inequality signs are not pointing in the same direction, multiply one equation by -1 so that they are.
2. Multiplying by any negative number changes the sign of the inequality.
3. Inequalities may be added to eliminate terms, but *not* subtracted.

Examples:
To solve

$$3y + 2x > 4 \quad \dots \quad (1)$$
$$2y - 3x < 6 \quad \dots \quad (2)$$

To make the signs point the same way multiply (2) by -1

$$-2y + 3x > -6 \quad \dots \quad (3)$$

To eliminate y multiply (1) by 2 and (3) by 3

$$6y + 4x > \quad 8 \quad \dots \quad (4)$$
$$-6y + 9x > -18 \quad \dots \quad (5)$$

Adding (4) and (5)

$$13x > -10$$

$$x > -\tfrac{10}{13}$$

x cannot be eliminated since the inequalities cannot be subtracted. Hence y may have any value.

Graphical solution
To solve

$$3y + 2x > 6 \quad \dots \quad (1)$$
$$4y - x \leqslant 5 \quad \dots \quad (2)$$

Draw the two lines. Choose a convenient point and substitute the co-ordinates into the inequalities to see which side of the line the inequality holds for.

Note that the boundary line of $3y + 2x > 6$ is dotted since $3y + 2x \neq 6$

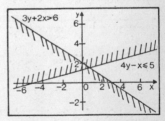

Figure 16

Linear programming This is the name given to a graphical technique used for solving problems involving inequalities. It is best understood by an example.

Example. A firm makes two products x and y. Not more than 20 kg of x and y can be manufactured in a day. It must make at least 8 kg of x and 4 kg of y in a day. 1 kg of x requires 20 machine hours and 1 kg of y requires 30 machine hours. The total number of machine hours that can be worked in 1 day is not more than 450. 1 kg of x produces £10 profit, 1 kg of y, £8 profit. Calculate the number of kilograms of x and y to be manufactured per day for maximum profit.
Solution Write the information given in terms of the inequality:

$$x \geqslant 8 \quad y \geqslant 4 \quad x + y \leqslant 20 \quad 20x + 30y \leqslant 450 \quad \text{i.e. } 2x + 3y \leqslant 45$$

Draw on a graph the lines $x = 8$, $y = 4$, $x + y = 20$, $2x + 3y = 45$ and shade the areas which do not satisfy the inequalities.

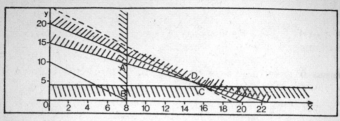

Figure 17

The lines $10x + 8y = c$ represent a series of parallel lines called profit lines. Choose a convenient value of c say 80 and plot this line. Then the line representing maximum profit will be parallel to this line passing through points in or on the area $ABCD$ and as far from the origin as possible i.e. the line passing through the point D which has co-ordinates (15, 5).

the maximum profit = £150 + £40 = £190

Matrices

A matrix is a rectangular array of elements arranged in rows and columns and enclosed by a bracket.

Order of a matrix = number of rows × number of columns.
A matrix with x rows and y columns is an 'x by y' matrix e.g.

$$\begin{pmatrix} 2 & 4 & 6 \\ 10 & 13 & 17 \end{pmatrix}$$

2 × 3 matrix

'2 by 3' matrix

$$\begin{pmatrix} 4 & 2 \\ 3 & 7 \\ 9 & 11 \end{pmatrix}$$

3 × 2 matrix

'3 by 2' matrix

A column matrix is one which contains only one column of elements i.e. each row only contains one element. A column matrix has an order of the form $m \times 1$ e.g.

$$\begin{pmatrix} 12 \\ 15 \end{pmatrix}$$

2 × 1 matrix

$$\begin{pmatrix} 2 \\ 3 \\ 6 \end{pmatrix}$$

3 × 1 matrix

A row matrix is one which contains only one row of elements i.e. each column only contains one element. A row matrix has an order of the form $1 \times n$ e.g.

$$(7 \quad 12 \quad 20)$$

1 × 3 matrix

$$(2 \quad 7 \quad 11 \quad 14)$$

1 × 4 matrix

Equality of matrices Two matrices are equal when and only when corresponding elements of the matrices are equal.

A square matrix is one which has the same number of rows as columns e.g.

$$\begin{pmatrix} 2 & 6 \\ 7 & 8 \end{pmatrix}$$

2 × 2 matrix

$$\begin{pmatrix} 3 & 7 & 6 \\ 2 & 7 & 9 \\ 4 & 9 & 2 \end{pmatrix}$$

3 × 3 matrix

Addition and subtraction of matrices

1. Two matrices may be added or subtracted only when they are of the same order i.e. when they have the same number of rows as each other and the same number of columns.

2. The elements in corresponding positions are added or subtracted e.g.

$$\begin{pmatrix} 2 & 3 \\ 7 & 8 \\ 4 & 6 \end{pmatrix} + \begin{pmatrix} 7 & 4 \\ 5 & 6 \\ 2 & 1 \end{pmatrix} = \begin{pmatrix} 2+7 & 3+4 \\ 7+5 & 8+6 \\ 4+2 & 6+1 \end{pmatrix} = \begin{pmatrix} 9 & 7 \\ 12 & 14 \\ 6 & 7 \end{pmatrix}$$

Commutative nature of matrix addition

Matrix addition is commutative i.e. $A + B = B + A$

$$\begin{pmatrix} 2 & 4 \\ 8 & 6 \end{pmatrix} + \begin{pmatrix} 3 & 2 \\ 6 & 1 \end{pmatrix} = \begin{pmatrix} 5 & 6 \\ 14 & 7 \end{pmatrix} \; ; \; \begin{pmatrix} 3 & 2 \\ 6 & 1 \end{pmatrix} + \begin{pmatrix} 2 & 4 \\ 8 & 6 \end{pmatrix} = \begin{pmatrix} 5 & 6 \\ 14 & 7 \end{pmatrix}$$

Multiplication of a matrix by a constant or number

Each element of the matrix is multiplied by the constant or number. e.g.

$$k \times \begin{pmatrix} p & q \\ r & s \end{pmatrix} = \begin{pmatrix} kp & kq \\ kr & ks \end{pmatrix} \qquad 3 \times \begin{pmatrix} 4 & 7 \\ 5 & 3 \end{pmatrix} = \begin{pmatrix} 12 & 21 \\ 15 & 9 \end{pmatrix}$$

Multiplication by matrices

1. Two matrices may be multiplied together only if the number of columns of the first matrix is equal to the number of rows of the second matrix. When this is not the case the matrices are said to be incompatible.

2. Each element of every row of the first matrix is multiplied by the corresponding element in every column of the second matrix. The sum of the products for any row and column are written in the position where that row and column intersect e.g.

$$\begin{pmatrix} 2 & 3 \\ 6 & 7 \end{pmatrix} \times \begin{pmatrix} a & b \\ c & d \end{pmatrix} = \begin{pmatrix} 2a + 3c & 2b + 3d \\ 6a + 7c & 6b + 7d \end{pmatrix}$$

3. When AB is evaluated, B is said to be pre-multiplied by A. When BA is evaluated, B is said to be post-multiplied by A.

Non-commutative nature of matrix multiplication

In general, matrix multiplication is not commutative i.e. $AB \neq BA$. e.g.

$$\begin{pmatrix} 4 & 2 \\ 3 & 6 \end{pmatrix} \begin{pmatrix} 5 & 3 \\ 1 & 4 \end{pmatrix} = \begin{pmatrix} 22 & 20 \\ 21 & 33 \end{pmatrix} \quad \text{but} \quad \begin{pmatrix} 5 & 3 \\ 1 & 4 \end{pmatrix} \begin{pmatrix} 4 & 2 \\ 3 & 6 \end{pmatrix} = \begin{pmatrix} 29 & 28 \\ 16 & 26 \end{pmatrix}$$

The zero or null matrix, O, is a *square matrix* in which each element has the value zero. The zero matrix can be of any order. It has the following properties:

1. A matrix multiplied by the zero matrix gives the zero matrix. i.e. $AO = OA = O$, an exception to the rule is that $AB \neq BA$.

2. A matrix added to the zero matrix remains unchanged i.e. $A + O = O + A = A$.

The unit or identity matrix, I, is a *square matrix* in which each element of the principal diagonal is unity and each other element is zero. It can be of any order i.e.

$$I = \begin{pmatrix} 1 & 0 \\ 0 & 1 \end{pmatrix} \qquad\qquad I = \begin{pmatrix} 1 & 0 & 0 \\ 0 & 1 & 0 \\ 0 & 0 & 1 \end{pmatrix}$$

2 × 2 matrix   3 × 3 matrix

Pre- or post-multiplication of a matrix by the unit matrix leaves the matrix unchanged i.e. $AI = IA = A$, another exception to the rule that $AB \neq BA$.

The determinant of a matrix, $A = \begin{pmatrix} a & b \\ c & d \end{pmatrix}$, is the numerical value of $ad - bc$. Only a square matrix can have a determinant. For example, if $A = \begin{pmatrix} 7 & 2 \\ 2 & 4 \end{pmatrix}$ then its determinant $= 7 \times 4 - (2 \times 2) = 24$.

A singular matrix is one for which the determinant is zero. The matrix has no inverse. Examples of singular matrices are

$$\begin{pmatrix} 8 & 6 \\ 4 & 3 \end{pmatrix} \quad \text{and} \quad \begin{pmatrix} 7 & 14 \\ 3 & 6 \end{pmatrix}$$

In both matrices the product of the elements of one diagonal is equal to the product of the elements of the other diagonal.

The inverse of a square matrix A, written A^{-1}, is that matrix which when multiplied by the original matrix produces the identity matrix i.e. $A \times A^{-1} = A^{-1} \times A = I$.

Procedure for finding the inverse of a matrix whose determinant is not equal to zero.

1. Interchange the elements of the leading diagonal.
2. Reverse the sign of the elements of the other diagonal.
3. Divide this matrix by the determinant of the original matrix.

33

Example, to find the inverse of $A = \begin{pmatrix} 7 & 4 \\ 3 & 2 \end{pmatrix}$

Step 1. A becomes $\begin{pmatrix} 2 & 4 \\ 3 & 7 \end{pmatrix}$ *Step 2.* Matrix becomes $\begin{pmatrix} 2 & -4 \\ -3 & 7 \end{pmatrix}$

Step 3. Determinant of A is $2 \times 7 - 3 \times 4 = 2$. Dividing $\begin{pmatrix} 2 & -4 \\ -3 & 7 \end{pmatrix}$

by 2 gives $\begin{pmatrix} 1 & -2 \\ -\frac{3}{2} & \frac{7}{2} \end{pmatrix}$ which is the inverse of A.

To check $\begin{pmatrix} 7 & 4 \\ 3 & 2 \end{pmatrix} \times \begin{pmatrix} 1 & -2 \\ -\frac{3}{2} & \frac{7}{2} \end{pmatrix} = \begin{pmatrix} 7-6 & -14+14 \\ 3-3 & -6+7 \end{pmatrix} = \begin{pmatrix} 1 & 0 \\ 0 & 1 \end{pmatrix}$

Solution of simultaneous equations using matrices

Procedure:

1. Write the equations in matrix form.
2. Find the inverse of the first matrix on the left hand side of the equation.
3. Pre-multiply both sides of the matrix equation by this inverse.
4. Reduce the L.H.S. to $\begin{pmatrix} 1 & 0 \\ 0 & 1 \end{pmatrix}\begin{pmatrix} x \\ y \end{pmatrix}$ since $AA^{-1} = I$, the unit matrix.
5. Multiply the equation out reducing both sides to a column matrix.
6. Equate both sides of the equation to obtain x and y.

Example 1 To solve $3x + 2y = 12$
$$2x + 4y = 16$$

Writing the equations in matrix form
$$\begin{pmatrix} 3 & 2 \\ 2 & 4 \end{pmatrix}\begin{pmatrix} x \\ y \end{pmatrix} = \begin{pmatrix} 12 \\ 16 \end{pmatrix}$$

The inverse of $\begin{pmatrix} 3 & 2 \\ 2 & 4 \end{pmatrix}$ is $\frac{1}{8}\begin{pmatrix} 4 & -2 \\ -2 & 3 \end{pmatrix}$

Pre-multiplying the matrix equation by this inverse gives

$$\frac{1}{8}\begin{pmatrix} 4 & -2 \\ -2 & 3 \end{pmatrix}\begin{pmatrix} 3 & 2 \\ 2 & 4 \end{pmatrix}\begin{pmatrix} x \\ y \end{pmatrix} = \frac{1}{8}\begin{pmatrix} 4 & -2 \\ -2 & 3 \end{pmatrix}\begin{pmatrix} 12 \\ 16 \end{pmatrix}$$

Since $A^{-1} \times A = I$ we get

$$\begin{pmatrix} 1 & 0 \\ 0 & 1 \end{pmatrix}\begin{pmatrix} x \\ y \end{pmatrix} = \frac{1}{8}\begin{pmatrix} 4 & -2 \\ -2 & 3 \end{pmatrix}\begin{pmatrix} 12 \\ 16 \end{pmatrix}$$

Multiplying the matrices gives

$$\begin{pmatrix} x \\ y \end{pmatrix} = \frac{1}{8}\begin{pmatrix} 48 & -32 \\ -24 & +48 \end{pmatrix} = \frac{1}{8}\begin{pmatrix} 16 \\ 24 \end{pmatrix} = \begin{pmatrix} 2 \\ 3 \end{pmatrix}$$

$x = 2, y = 3$ is the solution.

Example 2

To solve $3x + 4y = 4$
$\qquad\quad 6x + 8y = 8$

Writing the equations in matrix form

$$\begin{pmatrix} 3 & 4 \\ 6 & 8 \end{pmatrix}\begin{pmatrix} x \\ y \end{pmatrix} = \begin{pmatrix} 4 \\ 8 \end{pmatrix}$$

The determinant of $\begin{pmatrix} 3 & 4 \\ 6 & 8 \end{pmatrix}$ is $24 - 24 = 0$. Therefore the matrix has no inverse. Observing the simultaneous equations again we can see that the first equation when multiplied by two gives the second equation. There are an infinite number of points (x, y) on the line and hence an infinite number of solutions.

The number of solutions of simultaneous equations

1. If the determinant is non-zero the equations will have one normal solution for x and y.
2. If the determinant is zero, there is either (i) an infinite number of solutions or (ii) no solutions. Examine the equations to determine which is true.

The transpose of a matrix A, written A', is the matrix obtained by interchanging the rows and columns of A. e.g.

$$\begin{pmatrix} 4 & 3 \\ 5 & 2 \end{pmatrix} \quad \text{is the transpose of} \quad \begin{pmatrix} 4 & 5 \\ 3 & 2 \end{pmatrix}$$

Geometry

Angles

An acute angle is an angle which is less than 90°, e.g. in figure 18(a) below angle *AOB* is acute.

A right angle is divided into 90 equal parts called degrees; a degree may be further subdivided into sixty equal parts known as minutes.

An obtuse angle is an angle which is between 90° and 180°, e.g. in figure 18(a) below angle *AOC* is obtuse.

A reflex angle is an angle which is between 180° and 360°, e.g. in figure 18(b) below the angle *AOB* indicated is reflex.

Complementary angles are two angles which add up to 90°.

Supplementary angles are two angles which add up to 180°, e.g. in figure 18(a) below angles *AOB* and *AOC* are supplementary angles.

Vertically opposite angles are angles of equal magnitude which face each other across the intersection of two straight lines, e.g. in figure 18(c), angles *x* and *w* are vertically opposite.

Alternate (adjacent) angles are angles of equal magnitude which lie on opposite sides of a line (called the transversal) which cuts two parallel lines, e.g. in figure 18(d) below *a* and *b* are alternate angles as are *c* and *d*.

Corresponding angles are angles of equal magnitude, which lie on the same side of two parallel lines cut by a straight line, e.g. in figure 18(d), angles *c* and *e* are corresponding angles.

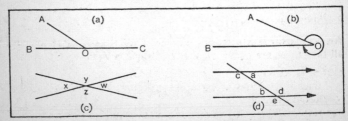

Figure 18

Parallel straight lines are lines which lie in the same plane and do not meet however far they are produced.

A transversal is a straight line which cuts two parallel lines.

Symmetry

Line symmetry If a figure reflected in a line maps on to itself, i.e. if for every point on a figure there exists a corresponding point on the other side of the line at an equal distance from it the figure has line symmetry. The line is known as an axis or line of symmetry e.g. an isosceles triangle has one line of symmetry.

Rotational symmetry If a figure when rotated about an axis maps on to itself, the figure possesses rotational symmetry. The order of rotational symmetry is equal to the number of times the figure maps on to itself during one complete revolution (360°). For example, an equilateral triangle maps on to itself once every 120° and therefore has rotational symmetry order 3.

Triangles

An acute angled triangle is one in which all the angles are less than 90°.

A right angled triangle is one in which one angle equals 90°. (The other two angles therefore add up to 90° and are hence complementary.)

An obtuse angled triangle is one in which one angle is greater than 90°.

A scalene triangle is one in which all the sides and angles are different.

An isosceles triangle has two sides equal and two angles equal. *Symmetry.* It has:
1. 1 line of symmetry
2. rotational symmetry order 0

An equilateral triangle is one in which all the sides are equal and all the angles are equal. Hence each angle is equal to 60°.

Symmetry. It has:
1. 3 lines of symmetry which meet at a point G; this is also the axis of rotational symmetry.
2. rotational symmetry order 3, since the triangle maps on to itself once every 120° of rotation, i.e. 3 times in one revolution.

A vertex is the angular point of a figure.
For example, a triangle has three vertices, a quadrilateral has four vertices.

Congruent figures are figures which are identical in size and shape. (A figure and its image under rotation, reflection and translation are congruent.)

Congruent triangles Triangles are congruent if they possess one of the following sets of features:

1. Three sides of one respectively equal to three sides of the other (SSS).

2. Two angles of one triangle respectively equal to two angles of the other and the side of one triangle equal to the corresponding side of the other (AAS).

3. Two sides of one triangle respectively equal to two sides of the other and the angle between the equal sides (included angle) also equal (SAS).

4. Two right-angled triangles are congruent if their hypotenuses are equal and another side of one triangle equal to the corresponding side of the other triangle (RHS).

Similar figures have the same shape but differ in size. Corresponding dimensions are in the same ratio i.e. one figure is an enlargement of the other.

Similar triangles Triangles are similar if they possess one of the following sets of features:

1. The angles of each triangle are equal.
2. The corresponding sides of each triangle are in the same ratio.
3. Two pairs of corresponding sides are in the same ratio and the angles between them equal.

Areas and volumes of similar figures In general, if the sides of similar figures are in the ratio $1:n$

the ratio of the areas = $1:n^2$,
the ratio of the volumes = $1:n^3$.

Theorems for triangles
1. The sum of the angles in a triangle is $180°$.
2. The exterior angle of a triangle is equal to the sum of the two interior opposite angles.
3. The angles opposite the two equal sides of an isosceles triangle are also equal.

4. The straight line which joins the middle points of two sides of a triangle is parallel to, and equal to half, the third side.

5. A straight line drawn parallel to one side of a triangle divides the other two sides in the same ratio.

6. If one angle of a triangle is bisected the bisector divides the opposite side in the same ratio as the sides containing the angle.

7. If two triangles are equiangular, corresponding sides are proportional, and the triangles are similar.

8. The areas of similar triangles are proportional to the squares on the corresponding sides.

9. The area of a triangle is half the area of the rectangle on the same base and having the same altitude.

10. **Pythagoras' theorem** In a right-angled triangle, the square on the hypotenuse is equal to the sum of the squares on the other two sides. $a^2 = b^2 + c^2$

11. **Converse of Pythagoras** If the square on one side of a triangle is equal to the sum of the squares on the other two sides, the angle included between these two sides is a right angle.

12. In any triangle, the square on the side opposite an acute angle is equal to the sum of the squares on the other two sides, less twice the product of one of these sides and the projection of the other upon it

$$a^2 = b^2 + c^2 - 2bc \cos A$$

13. In any obtuse-angled triangle, the square on the side opposite the obtuse angle is equal to the sum of the squares on the other two sides plus twice the product of one of these sides and the projection of the other upon it (figure 19a).

$$a^2 = b^2 + c^2 + 2bc \cos A$$

14. In any triangle, the sum of the squares on two sides is equal to twice the square on half the third side, together with twice the square on the median which bisects the third side (figure 19b).

$$b^2 + c^2 = 2a^2 + 2m^2$$

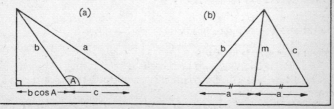

Figure 19

39

Polygons

A polygon is a plane figure with any number of sides. A polygon with 3 sides is a triangle, with four sides a quadrilateral, with 5 sides a **pentagon**, 6 sides a **hexagon** and 8 sides an **octagon**.

A convex polygon is one in which each angle is less than 180°.

A regular polygon has all sides equal and all angles equal.

Quadrilaterals

A quadrilateral is a plane figure bounded by four straight lines.

A trapezium is a quadrilateral which has one pair of parallel sides. It has no lines of symmetry or axes of rotational symmetry.

A kite is a quadrilateral which has no sides parallel but which has two pairs of adjacent sides equal.
Properties
1. The diagonals are at right angles; one of the diagonals is bisected by the other.
2. The angles A and C are bisected by the diagonal AC.
Symmetry
1. It has 1 line of symmetry.
2. It has rotational symmetry order 0.

A parallelogram is a quadrilateral with opposite sides parallel.
Properties
1. The opposite sides are equal.
2. The opposite angles are equal.
3. The diagonals bisect each other.
4. A diagonal bisects the parallelogram.
Symmetry
1. It has no lines of symmetry.
2. It has rotational symmetry order 2 about point O.

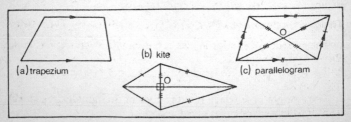

(a) trapezium   (b) kite   (c) parallelogram

Figure 20

A rhombus is a parallelogram with all its sides equal, but the angles are not right angles.

Properties. It has all the properties of a parallelogram and in addition:

1. The diagonals bisect each other at right angles.
2. The diagonals bisect the angles of the rhombus.

Symmetry

1. It has two lines of symmetry which are the diagonals of the rhombus.
2. It has rotational symmetry order 2 about point O.

A rectangle is a parallelogram in which all the angles are right angles.

Properties It has all the properties of a parallelogram and in addition its diagonals are equal in length.

Symmetry

1. It has two lines of symmetry, m_1 and m_2.
2. It has rotational symmetry order 2 about point O.

A square is a rectangle with all sides equal.

Properties It has all the properties of the parallelogram, rhombus and rectangle.

Symmetry

1. It has four lines of symmetry m_1 m_2 and the diagonals.
2. It has rotational symmetry order 4 about point O. (i.e. it maps on to itself once every 90°).

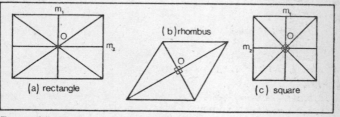

Figure 21. (a) rectangle (b) rhombus (c) square

Theorems connected with polygons and parallelograms

1. The sum of the interior angles of a convex polygon of n sides is $(2n - 4)$ right angles.
2. The sum of the exterior angles of a convex polygon with n sides is 4 right angles.
3. The straight lines which join the ends of two equal and parallel lines are themselves equal and parallel.

4. The opposite sides and angles of a parallelogram are equal, and each diagonal bisects the parallelogram.

5. The diagonals of a rhombus bisect each other.

6. Parallelograms on the same base and between the same parallels are equal in area.

Circle

A circle is a plane figure formed by a point which moves so that its distance from a fixed point is constant.

The circumference is the boundary line of a circle.

A radius is the distance from the centre of the circle to the circumference.

A diameter of a circle is a straight line passing through the centre joining two points on the circumference.

A chord is a straight line joining any two points on the circumference.

An arc is part of the circumference.

A segment is a part of a circle bounded by a chord and an arc.

An angle in a segment is formed by two straight lines joining the ends of the chord to any point on the arc of the segment.

A sector is a part of a circle enclosed by two radii and an arc.

A secant of a circle is a straight line of indefinite length which cuts the circle in two points.

A tangent to a circle is a straight line which touches the circumference at one point only.

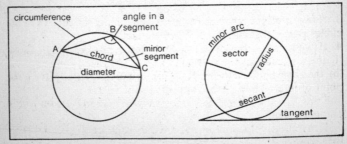

Figure 22

Theorems connected with the chord of a circle

1. The perpendicular bisector of a chord passes through the centre of a circle.
2. The perpendicular drawn from the centre of a circle to a chord bisects that chord.
3. One circle and one circle only can pass through any three points not in the same straight line.
4. Equal chords of a circle are equidistant from the centre.
5. Chords which are equidistant from the centre of a circle are equal.
6. Equal chords stand on equal arcs.

Theorems connected with the angles of a circle

1. The angle which an arc subtends at the centre of a circle is twice the angle subtended by the arc at any other point on the remaining part of the circumference.
2. Angles subtended by an arc of a circle at the circumference are equal.
3. The angle in a semi-circle is a right angle.
4. The opposite angles of a quadrilateral inscribed in a circle (cyclic quadrilateral) add up to 180°.
5. The exterior angle of a cyclic quadrilateral is equal to the interior opposite angle of the quadrilateral.
6. The angle subtended by an arc at the circumference of a circle is proportional to the length of the arc.

Theorems connected with tangents of a circle

1. The tangent to a circle at any point is perpendicular to the radius drawn at the point of contact.
2. The angle between a tangent to a circle and the chord drawn through the point of contact is equal to the angle in the alternate segment.
3. If two circles touch each other the line joining the centres of the circles passes through the point of contact.
4. If two tangents are drawn to a circle from a point outside a circle;
(i) the tangents are equal in length
(ii) the angle between the tangents is bisected by the line joining the point of intersection of the tangents to the centre
(iii) this line also bisects the angle between the radii drawn to the points of contact.
5. If two chords of a circle intersect either inside or outside the circle the rectangle contained by the parts of one is equal to the rectangle contained by the parts of the other.

Loci

A locus is a set of points which satisfies given conditions, or the path of a point which moves in accordance with a given rule.

Examples of loci

1. The locus of a point which moves in a plane at a fixed distance from a fixed point is the circumference of a circle (or in three dimensions a sphere). The fixed point is the centre of the circle and the fixed distance the radius.

2. The locus of a point which is equidistant from two fixed points is the perpendicular bisector of a straight line joining the two points.

3. The locus of a point which is equidistant from two fixed intersecting straight lines is the pair of straight lines which bisects the angles between the two given lines (figure 23).

4. The locus of a point C which moves on one side of a given line AB so that the angle ACB is constant is an arc of a circle passing through A and B.

5. The locus of a point which moves so that it is equidistant from a point F and a straight line AB is a parabola (figure 23).

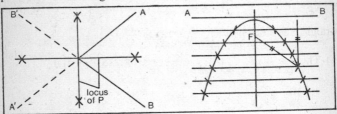

Figure 23

Graphs

Straight line

The equation of a straight line may be written in two forms—the gradient/intercept form and the intercept form.

(i) The *gradient/intercept form of the equation for a straight line is*

$$y = mx + c$$

where m is the gradient and
c is the intercept on the y axis

The graph of $y = \frac{7}{5}x - 3$ is a straight line with gradient $\frac{7}{5}$ and y intercept -3 (figure 24).
To draw the graph two points are required which are obtained as follows:
1. The position of the y intercept ($= -3$) is marked.
2. A point with co-ordinates $(5, 4)$ is marked. This point will lie on the

straight line since gradient of a line $= \dfrac{y}{x} = \dfrac{7}{5}$.

(ii) The *intercept form of the equation for a straight line is*

$$\frac{x}{a} + \frac{y}{b} = 1$$

where a is the intercept on the x axis and
b is the intercept on the y axis

The graph of $\dfrac{x}{4} + \dfrac{y}{10} = 1$ is a straight line with an x intercept of 4 and a y intercept of 10 (figure 24).

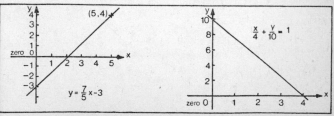

Figure 24. Straight line graphs

Parabola

A parabola is the graph of a quadratic function $ax^2 + bx + c$, where a, b and c are constants. b and c may be zero.

Examples:

$$y = x^2$$
$$y = 3x^2$$
$$y = x^2 - 1$$
$$y = (3x + 2)(x - 4)$$

To sketch a parabola three points are required which are obtained by finding the intersection of the curve with the axes.

For example, to sketch the curve $y = 3x^2 - 7x - 6$

when $x = 0$, $y = -6$

when $y = 0$, $3x^2 - 7x - 6 = 0$
$$(x - 3)(3x + 2) = 0$$
$$x = 3 \text{ or } x = -\tfrac{2}{3}$$

The points $(0, -6)$, $(3, 0)$ and $(-\tfrac{2}{3}, 0)$ are marked on the graph and the parabola drawn.

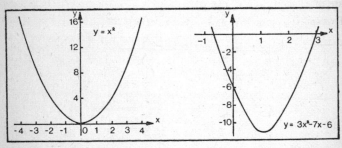

Figure 25. Parabolae

Rectangular Hyperbola

This is the graph of a function in which y varies inversely as x. When $x = 0$, $y = $ infinity

Examples: $xy = 13$

$$y = \frac{1}{x}$$

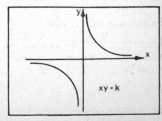

Figure 26. Rectangular Hyperbola

Circle

The equation of a circle with centre at the origin and radius r is

$$x^2 + y^2 = r^2 \quad \text{(figure 27)}.$$

The equation of a circle with centre at the point (x_1, y_1) and radius r is $(x - x_1)^2 + (y - y_1)^2 = r^2$ (figure 27).

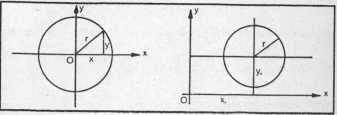

Figure 27

Cubic

Cubic equations contain an x or y term to the power 3. All other terms are of a lower power than 3.

Examples: $y = x^3$; $y = 3x^3 - 4x^2 + 3x + 1$

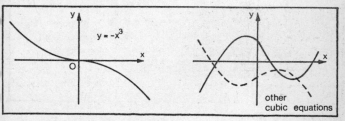

Figure 28. Graphs of cubic equations

Exponential curves

The exponential function is a^x where a is a constant and x is a variable.

When $x = 0$, $y = 1$

Examples: $y = 3^x$

$y = 8^x$

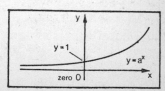

Figure 29. Exponential curve

47

Transformation Geometry

Transformations In any transformation a point, line, curve, plane or figure, A, maps on to its image A'. The mapping has one-to-one correspondence since for every point in A there is a unique point, A_1, in the image A'.

Isometric transformations

Isometries are transformations which preserve all lengths. Hence the shape, size, area and angles of the figure and its image are the same and they are therefore congruent. Translations, reflections, rotations are isometries. Enlargements, shear and stretch are not.

Invariant point or line The position of an invariant point or line remains unaltered by the transformation.

Translation If every point on a line, curve, plane or figure A, moves in a straight line the same distance and in the same direction then A has been translated to its image A'. The translation is described by the column vector
$$\begin{pmatrix} \text{displacement parallel to } x \text{ axis} \\ \text{displacement parallel to } y \text{ axis} \end{pmatrix}$$

A and its image A' are congruent. No point is invariant. Corresponding sides of the figure and image are parallel.

For example, in fig. 30 the translation of the line AB is described by the vector $\begin{pmatrix} 2 \\ 1 \end{pmatrix}$ since every point on the line has moved with a displacement equivalent to 2 units to the right and 1 unit upwards. The translation of triangle XYZ to $X'Y'Z'$ in fig. 30 is described by $\begin{pmatrix} -3 \\ 1 \end{pmatrix}$.

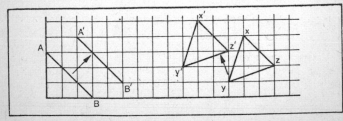

Figure 30   Translation

Reflection

The laws of mathematical reflection are very similar to those of physical reflection in plane mirrors, except that mirror lines are unlimited in length and reflection can take place on both sides.

1. Reflection of a point P in a line (figure 31) A point P is reflected in a line m such that the line joining P and its image P' is bisected perpendicularly by m. m is called the mediator of PP'.

2. Reflection of a point in two perpendicular axes Four points are obtained with the co-ordinates as indicated. The y axis is the mediator of the lines PP_1 and P_1P_2. The x axis is the mediator of the lines PP_3 and P_2P_3.

3. Reflection in angled lines (figure 31) If the angle between 2 mirrors is θ; then the angle between the point and its second image Q_2 is 2θ. This is equivalent to a rotation of 2θ.

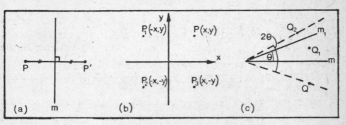

Figure 31

4. Reflection in parallel lines (figure 32) If the distance between the two lines is d then the distance between Q and Q_2 is $2d$.

5. Reflection of a point in the lines $y = x$ **and** $y = -x$ (figure 32) Reflection in the line $y = x$ maps (x, y) on to (y, x). Reflection in the line $y = -x$ maps (x, y) on to $(-y, -x)$.

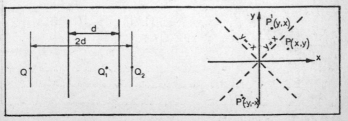

Figure 32

6. Reflection of a triangle in a line (figure 33)

Properties of the triangle and its image:

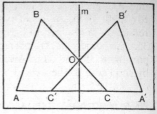

Figure 33

1. The image is laterally inverted.
2. Triangles ABC and $A'B'C'$ are congruent.
3. The mirror line, m, is the mediator (perpendicular bisector) of the line segment joining any point to its image e.g. m bisects AA', CC', BB'.
4. Points lying on m are invariant i.e. they are their own images.
5. m bisects the angle between any line and its image, e.g. m bisects BOB'.

Rotation (figure 34)

1. The positive direction is anti-clockwise.
2. The centre of rotation D is invariant. It is the only point on the figure which does not move.
3. The centre of rotation lies on the point of intersection of the perpendicular bisectors of the lines joining any point to its image under rotation.
4. The image $A'B'C'$ under rotation is directly congruent to ABC (contrast the image in a mirror line which is laterally inverted).
5. Every line is rotated through the same angle of rotation.
6. In general

$+ 90°$ rotation about $(0, 0)$ maps (x, y) on to $(-y, x)$
$+ 180°$ rotation about $(0, 0)$ maps (x, y) on to $(-x, -y)$
$+ 270°$ rotation about $(0, 0)$ maps (x, y) on to $(y, -x)$

A $+ 270°$ rotation is the same as a $-90°$ rotation.

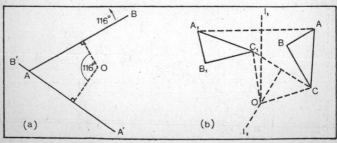

Figure 34. Rotation

Glide reflection is produced by a translation parallel to the mirror line followed by a reflection in the line. In figure 35, the object is translated parallel to the x axis followed by reflection in the axis.

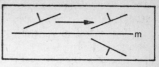

Figure 35

Non-isometric transformations: enlargement, shearing and stretch:

Enlargements are transformations about a centre of magnification (enlargement) which preserve all angles but which multiply lengths by a scale factor.

Figure 36 shows ABC and its enlargements for scale factors of $-1, \frac{1}{2}$ and 2. Enlargements possess the following characteristics:

1. The centre of magnification, O, is the only invariant point.
2. A positive scale factor produces an erect image on the same side of O as the object.

A negative scale factor produces an inverted image on the opposite side of O to the object.

3. Every image of B lies on the line OB, and likewise for every other point and its image under enlargement.
4. The object and its images are similar, i.e. corresponding angles are equal and corresponding sides proportional.

5. $\dfrac{\text{Length of side in image}}{\text{Length of corresponding side in object}} = \text{scale factor}$

$$\frac{\text{Area of image}}{\text{Area of object}} = (\text{scale factor})^2$$

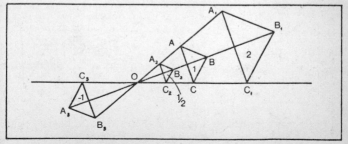

Figure 36. Enlargements

Shearing In a shear, one line of the figure is invariant. All other points on the figure are displaced parallel to the invariant line and through a distance proportional to their distance from the line. Shearing does not alter the area of a figure or the volume of a solid. For example, in figure

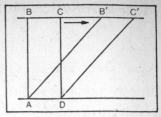

Figure 37. Shearing

37 the rectangle *ABCD* has been transformed by a shear parallel to the base *AD* to produce the parallelogram *AB'C'D*. Since area *ABB'* equals area of *CC'D* this shows that the areas of a rectangle and parallelogram on the same base and of the same height are equal.

Stretch in a stretch, one line of the figure is invariant. All other lines move in a direction perpendicular to the invariant line, i.e. stretch is an enlargement in one direction only. For example, in figure 38 the line *PR* is the invariant line. *PRS* has been stretched in the vertical direction by a scale factor of 2. In figure 38(b) *PQ* is the invariant line. *PQRS* has been stretched in the horizontal direction by a scale factor of 2.

Area of stretched figure = Area of original figure × scale factor

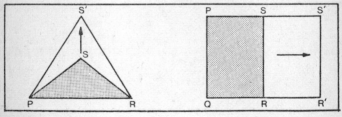

Figure 3   Stretch

The product of transformations *TMR* where *T*, *M* and *R* are specified transformations requires by convention that *R* be carried out first, followed by *M*, then *T*. One cannot assume that *TMR* = *RMT*.

The identity transformation, *I*, is a transformation which returns a figure to its original position with the original shape and size.

Transformation Matrices

A 2×2 matrix can be used to transform any point in the (x, y) plane. The point is written as a column vector $\begin{pmatrix} x \\ y \end{pmatrix}$ and pre-multiplied by the 2×2 matrix.

Reflection

Reflection in the x axis

$$\text{Use} \quad \begin{pmatrix} 1 & 0 \\ 0 & -1 \end{pmatrix}$$

We require (x, y) to map on to $(x, -y)$

$$\begin{pmatrix} 1 & 0 \\ 0 & -1 \end{pmatrix} \begin{pmatrix} x \\ y \end{pmatrix} = \begin{pmatrix} x + 0 \\ 0 - y \end{pmatrix} = \begin{pmatrix} x \\ y \end{pmatrix}$$

Reflection in the y axis

$$\text{Use} \quad \begin{pmatrix} -1 & 0 \\ 0 & 1 \end{pmatrix}$$

We require (x, y) to map on to $(-x, y)$

$$\begin{pmatrix} -1 & 0 \\ 0 & 1 \end{pmatrix} \begin{pmatrix} x \\ y \end{pmatrix} = \begin{pmatrix} -x + 0 \\ 0 + y \end{pmatrix} = \begin{pmatrix} -x \\ y \end{pmatrix}$$

Reflection in the line y = x

$$\text{Use} \quad \begin{pmatrix} 0 & 1 \\ 1 & 0 \end{pmatrix}$$

We require (x, y) to map on to (y, x)

$$\begin{pmatrix} 0 & 1 \\ 1 & 0 \end{pmatrix} \begin{pmatrix} x \\ y \end{pmatrix} = \begin{pmatrix} 0 + y \\ x + 0 \end{pmatrix} = \begin{pmatrix} y \\ x \end{pmatrix}.$$

Reflection in the line y = −x

$$\text{Use} \quad \begin{pmatrix} 0 & -1 \\ -1 & 0 \end{pmatrix}$$

We require (x, y) to map on to $(-y, -x)$

$$\begin{pmatrix} 0 & -1 \\ -1 & 0 \end{pmatrix} \begin{pmatrix} x \\ y \end{pmatrix} = \begin{pmatrix} 0 - y \\ -x & 0 \end{pmatrix} = \begin{pmatrix} -y \\ -x \end{pmatrix}$$

Rotation

Rotation about the origin O clockwise through **+90°**.

$$\text{Use} \begin{pmatrix} 0 & -1 \\ 1 & 0 \end{pmatrix}$$

We require (x, y) to map on to $(-y, x)$

$$\begin{pmatrix} 0 & -1 \\ 1 & 0 \end{pmatrix} \begin{pmatrix} x \\ y \end{pmatrix} = \begin{pmatrix} 0 & -y \\ x & 0 \end{pmatrix} = \begin{pmatrix} -y \\ x \end{pmatrix}$$

Rotation about the origin O through **180°** (either direction)

$$\text{Use} \begin{pmatrix} -1 & 0 \\ 0 & -1 \end{pmatrix}$$

We require (x, y) to map on to $(-x, -y)$

$$\begin{pmatrix} -1 & 0 \\ 0 & -1 \end{pmatrix} \begin{pmatrix} x \\ y \end{pmatrix} = \begin{pmatrix} -x + 0 \\ 0 - y \end{pmatrix} = \begin{pmatrix} -x \\ -y \end{pmatrix}$$

Rotation about the origin through **270°** (or **−90°**)

$$\text{Use} \begin{pmatrix} 0 & 1 \\ -1 & 0 \end{pmatrix}$$

We require (x, y) to map on to $(y, -x)$

$$\begin{pmatrix} 0 & 1 \\ -1 & 0 \end{pmatrix} \begin{pmatrix} x \\ y \end{pmatrix} = \begin{pmatrix} 0 & y \\ -x & 0 \end{pmatrix} = \begin{pmatrix} y \\ -x \end{pmatrix}.$$

Enlargement, translation, shear and stretch

Enlargement For an enlargement scale factor k and centre $(0, 0)$

$$\text{Use} \begin{pmatrix} k & 0 \\ 0 & k \end{pmatrix}$$

E.g. if the scale factor is 2 then $(3, 2)$ should map on to $(6, 4)$

$$\begin{pmatrix} 2 & 0 \\ 0 & 2 \end{pmatrix} \begin{pmatrix} 3 \\ 2 \end{pmatrix} = \begin{pmatrix} 6 + 0 \\ 0 + 4 \end{pmatrix} = \begin{pmatrix} 6 \\ 4 \end{pmatrix}$$

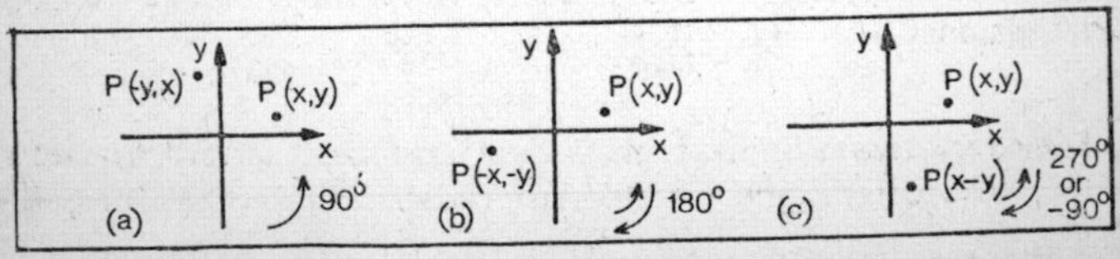

Figure 39.

Translation To translate the point (x, y) 2 units in the $+x$ direction and 4 units in the $+y$ direction, we add 2 and 4 to the x and y coordinates respectively. Hence

$$\begin{pmatrix} x \\ y \end{pmatrix} + \begin{pmatrix} 2 \\ 4 \end{pmatrix} = \begin{pmatrix} x + 2 \\ y + 4 \end{pmatrix}$$

Shear (i) A figure whose base is an invariant line on the x axis may be sheared parallel to the x axis by using

$$\begin{pmatrix} 1 & a \\ 0 & 1 \end{pmatrix}$$

This leaves all points on the x axis unaltered. Each value of a gives a different shear.

(ii) A figure whose base is an invariant line on the y axis may be sheared parallel to the y axis by using

$$\begin{pmatrix} 1 & 0 \\ b & 1 \end{pmatrix}$$

Stretch (i) A figure whose base is an invariant line on the x axis may be stretched parallel to the y axis premultiplying by

$$\begin{pmatrix} 1 & 0 \\ 0 & b \end{pmatrix}$$

(ii) A figure whose base is an invariant line on the y axis may be stretched parallel to the x axis by premultiplying by

$$\begin{pmatrix} a & 0 \\ 0 & 1 \end{pmatrix}$$

The product of transformations To obtain the product of transformations multiply the matrices which give them, e.g.

if $M = \begin{pmatrix} 3 & 0 \\ 0 & 3 \end{pmatrix}$ and $E = \begin{pmatrix} -1 & 0 \\ 0 & 1 \end{pmatrix}$ then

$$ME(x, y) = \begin{pmatrix} 3 & 0 \\ 0 & 3 \end{pmatrix}\begin{pmatrix} -1 & 0 \\ 0 & 1 \end{pmatrix}\begin{pmatrix} x \\ y \end{pmatrix} = \begin{pmatrix} -3 & 0 \\ 0 & 3 \end{pmatrix}\begin{pmatrix} x \\ y \end{pmatrix} = \begin{pmatrix} -3x \\ 3y \end{pmatrix}$$

The point (x, y) has been mapped on to the point $(-3x, 3y)$. It cannot be assumed that $ME = EM$.

Identity transformation is the transformation which returns the figure to its original position, size and shape. It is equivalent to the

unit matrix, I which is $\begin{pmatrix} 1 & 0 \\ 0 & 1 \end{pmatrix}$

Vectors

A scalar quantity has magnitude only.
Examples of scalar quantities: mass, distance, speed and temperature.

A vector quantity has both magnitude and direction.
Examples of vector quantities: velocity, force, momentum and displacement.

Representation of vectors A vector can be represented by a line, whose length represents the magnitude of the vector and whose direction, indicated by an arrow, represents the direction of the vector.

Vector notation

There are several ways of denoting a vector. For example, the vector represented by the line AB in figure 40 may be represented in any of the following ways:

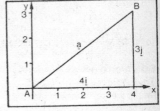

Figure 40

$$\overrightarrow{AB}, \ \mathbf{a}, \ \begin{pmatrix} 4 \\ 3 \end{pmatrix}$$

or $4\mathbf{i} + 3\mathbf{j}$ (position vector)
$\mathbf{i}$ and $\mathbf{j}$ are the unit vectors.

The modulus of a vector AB written $|\overrightarrow{AB}|$ or $|\mathbf{a}|$ is the magnitude of the vector, i.e. the length of $\overrightarrow{AB}$

$$|\overrightarrow{AB}| = |\overrightarrow{BA}| \quad \text{or} \quad |\mathbf{a}| = |-\mathbf{a}|$$

By Pythagoras' theorem, the magnitude of the vector $\begin{pmatrix} 2 \\ 4 \end{pmatrix}$ is

$\sqrt{(2^2 + 4^2)}$. In 3D, the magnitude of vector $\begin{pmatrix} 1 \\ 3 \\ 2 \end{pmatrix}$ is

$\sqrt{(1^2 + 3^2 + 2^2)}$.

Direction of vector If θ is the direction $\overrightarrow{AB}$, represented by $\begin{pmatrix} 4 \\ 3 \end{pmatrix}$,

makes with the x axis (figure 40) then $\tan \theta = \frac{3}{4} = 0.75$.
$\theta = 36°52'$.

Parallel vectors Two vectors are parallel if they have the same direction, i.e. if they have the same gradient. For example, the vectors $\mathbf{a} = \begin{pmatrix} 3 \\ 2 \end{pmatrix}$ and $\mathbf{b} = \begin{pmatrix} 6 \\ 4 \end{pmatrix}$ are parallel since $\mathbf{b} = 2 \times \begin{pmatrix} 3 \\ 2 \end{pmatrix}$.

Addition of vectors (figure 41) $\overrightarrow{AB}$ added to $\overrightarrow{BC}$ gives vector $\overrightarrow{AC}$ i.e. $\overrightarrow{AB} + \overrightarrow{BC} = \overrightarrow{AC}$ or $\mathbf{a} + \mathbf{b} = \mathbf{c}$

or $\begin{pmatrix} 2 \\ 1 \end{pmatrix} + \begin{pmatrix} 1 \\ 3 \end{pmatrix} = \begin{pmatrix} 3 \\ 4 \end{pmatrix}$

Vector addition is commutative

$$\mathbf{a} + \mathbf{b} = \mathbf{b} + \mathbf{a}$$

Vector addition is associative

$$(\mathbf{a} + \mathbf{b}) + \mathbf{c} = \mathbf{a} + (\mathbf{b} + \mathbf{c})$$
$$= \mathbf{a} + \mathbf{b} + \mathbf{c}$$

The modulus equation for vector addition reads $|\mathbf{c}| = |\mathbf{a} + \mathbf{b}|$ and not $|\mathbf{c}| = |\mathbf{a}| + |\mathbf{b}|$

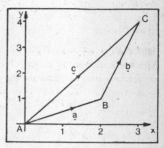

Figure 41

Subtraction of vectors
To subtract $\overrightarrow{AB} - \overrightarrow{BC}$ draw a line equal in magnitude but opposite in direction to $\overrightarrow{BC}$ (figure 42) and add the two vectors.

$\overrightarrow{AB} - \overrightarrow{BC} \Leftrightarrow \overrightarrow{AB} + \overrightarrow{BD} = \overrightarrow{AD}$

or in figures

$$\begin{pmatrix} 2 \\ 1 \end{pmatrix} - \begin{pmatrix} 1 \\ 3 \end{pmatrix} = \begin{pmatrix} 1 \\ -2 \end{pmatrix}$$

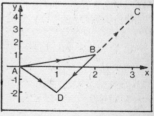

Figure 42

Parallelogram Law If $\overrightarrow{OA}$ and $\overrightarrow{OB}$ are two vectors represented in magnitude and direction by the sides of a parallelogram $OABC$ then the resultant of the vectors is represented in magnitude and direction by the diagonal $\overrightarrow{OC}$ of the parallelogram.

$$\overrightarrow{OB} + \overrightarrow{OA} = \overrightarrow{OC}$$

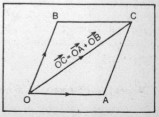

Figure 43

57

Multiplication by a scalar

The vector 3**a** has the same direction as **a** but three times the magnitude of **a**, i.e. $3\mathbf{a} = 3|\mathbf{a}|$. In figure 44

$\overrightarrow{PQ} = \overrightarrow{QR} = \mathbf{a} \quad \therefore \quad \overrightarrow{PR} = 2\mathbf{a}$

$\overrightarrow{RS} = \overrightarrow{ST} = \mathbf{b} \quad \therefore \quad \overrightarrow{RT} = 2\mathbf{b}$

$\overrightarrow{PT} = 2\mathbf{a} + 2\mathbf{b} = 2(\mathbf{a} + \mathbf{b})$

The distributive laws hold for scalar multiplication.

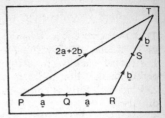

Figure 44

A position vector is used to define the distance and direction of a point A from another point O (the origin). In figure 45 $\overrightarrow{OA}$ or **a** is the position vector of A referred to O. If the coordinates of A are (3, 2) then

$OA = \begin{pmatrix} 3 \\ 2 \end{pmatrix}$

Position vectors may be added or subtracted. If A and B have position vectors

$\mathbf{a} = \begin{pmatrix} 3 \\ 2 \end{pmatrix} \quad \mathbf{b} = \begin{pmatrix} 1 \\ 4 \end{pmatrix} \quad \text{then}$

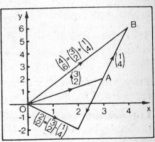

Figure 45

$\mathbf{a} + \mathbf{b} = \begin{pmatrix} 3 \\ 2 \end{pmatrix} + \begin{pmatrix} 1 \\ 4 \end{pmatrix} = \begin{pmatrix} 4 \\ 6 \end{pmatrix}$ $\qquad$ $\mathbf{a} - \mathbf{b} = \begin{pmatrix} 3 \\ 2 \end{pmatrix} - \begin{pmatrix} 1 \\ 4 \end{pmatrix} = \begin{pmatrix} 2 \\ -2 \end{pmatrix}$

Components (resolved parts, resolutes) of a vector If $\mathbf{c} = \mathbf{a} + \mathbf{b}$ then **a** and **b** are the components of **c**. These are usually taken at right angles to each other. In figure 46, $\overrightarrow{OQ}$, $\overrightarrow{OR}$ are the components of vector $\overrightarrow{OP}$.

Horizontal component
$\qquad = P\cos\theta$

Vertical component $= P\sin\theta$

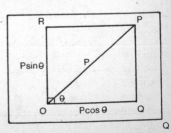

Figure 46

A unit vector is a vector with modulus 1.

i is the unit vector parallel to the x axis.

j is the unit vector parallel to the y axis.

The resultant of a system of vectors is that vector which has the same effect as all the vectors acting together. It is found as follows:
1. Resolve each vector into its components in two mutually perpendicular directions.
2. Find the resultant component in each of the two perpendicular directions.
3. Calculate the resultant of these two resultant components.

The equilibrant of a system of vectors is that vector which maintains the system in equilibrium. It is equal in magnitude but opposite in direction to the resultant.

Triangle of forces If three forces acting at a point are in equilibrium they can be represented in magnitude and direction by the sides of the triangle taken in order (figure 47).

Polygon of forces Any number of forces acting at a point can be represented by the sides of a polygon taken in order.

Lamis theorem If three forces P, Q, R act on a particle and α, β, γ are the angles between Q and R, R and P, P and Q respectively and the particle is in equilibrium (figure 47).

$$\frac{P}{\sin \alpha} = \frac{Q}{\sin \beta} = \frac{R}{\sin \gamma}$$

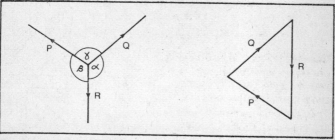

Figure 47

Arithmetic

Factors

The factors of a number are those numbers which divide into it exactly.

e.g. 2, 3, 6, 9 are the factors of 18; 2, 4, 5, 10 are the factors of 20

The prime factors of a number are the factors of that number which themselves belong to the set of prime numbers and which when multiplied together give the number.

e.g. $2 \times 3 \times 3$ are the prime factors of 18

Fractions

A fraction is made up of two numbers, the **numerator** on the top and the **denominator** on the bottom. The value of a fraction is not changed by multiplying or dividing both the numerator and denominator by the same number.

A proper fraction is one in which the numerator is less than the denominator, e.g. $\frac{2}{3}, \frac{1}{5}, \frac{11}{13}$

An improper fraction is one in which the numerator is greater than the denominator, e.g. $\frac{5}{3}, \frac{7}{4}, \frac{12}{11}$

Compound fraction (mixed number) is one which consists of an integer and a fraction, e.g. $2\frac{1}{8}, 3\frac{2}{3}$

The highest common factor (H.C.F.) is the largest number which divides exactly into two or more numbers, e.g. the H.C.F. of 16 and 24 is 8.

The lowest common multiple (L.C.M.) is the smallest number which is exactly divisible by two or more numbers, e.g. the L.C.M. of 14 and 4 is 28.

Cancelling a fraction is the division of both the numerator and the denominator by the same number. A fraction is expressed in its **lowest terms** when it is not possible to cancel it any further. Cancelling a fraction does not alter the value of the fraction, e.g.

$$\frac{8}{12} = \frac{4}{6} = \frac{2}{3} \quad \text{(expressed in its lowest terms)}$$

Addition and subtraction of fractions
1. Add the whole numbers.
2. Find the lowest common multiple (L.C.M.) of the fractions.
3. Express each fraction as a fraction having the L.C.M. as the denominator.
4. Add the numerators; the denominator is not added but remains the same as the L.C.M.
5. Cancel if possible.

e.g. $5\frac{3}{8} + 2\frac{2}{3} = 7 + \frac{3}{8} + \frac{2}{3} = 7 + \frac{9}{24} + \frac{16}{24} = 7\frac{25}{24} = 8\frac{1}{24}$

Multiplication of fractions
1. Change to improper fractions where necessary.
2. Multiply the numerators together and the denominators together.
3. Cancel where possible.

e.g. $3\frac{1}{2} \times 2\frac{2}{5} = \frac{7}{2} \times \frac{12}{5} = \frac{84}{10} = \frac{42}{5} = 8\frac{2}{5}$

Division by a fraction
1. Change numerator and denominator to improper fractions where necessary.
2. Invert the fraction in the denominator and change $\div$ sign to $\times$.
3. Proceed as for multiplication of fractions.

e.g. $4\frac{4}{5} \div \frac{6}{7} = \frac{24}{5} \div \frac{6}{7} = \frac{24}{5} \times \frac{7}{6} = \frac{28}{5} = 5\frac{3}{5}$

The reciprocal of a number a is $\dfrac{1}{a}$ which may be written a^{-1}.

Decimals

A decimal is a fraction in which the denominator is 10 or a power of 10. e.g. $0.36 = \frac{3}{10} + \frac{6}{100} = \frac{36}{100}$; $0.782 = \frac{7}{10} + \frac{8}{100} + \frac{2}{1000} = \frac{782}{1000}$

Decimal places (d.p.) refer to the digits including zero which follow the decimal point. Correct (or accurate) to 1 decimal place means correct to the nearest 0·1.

Number	Correct to		
	1 d.p. (nearest 0·1)	2 d.p. (nearest 0·01)	3 d.p. (nearest 0·001)
0·0682	0·1	0·07	0·068
2·3627	2·4	2·36	2·363
9·0076	9·0	9·01	9·008

Significant figures (S.F.)

The number of significant figures in any given number is the total number of figures including zero. The first significant figure is the first non-zero digit. Any zeros following this digit are counted as significant. However any zeros following the decimal point but preceding the first non zero digit are not significant. (See example (a) below.)

Examples

	Correct to		
Number	1 S.F.	2 S.F.	3 S.F.
(a) 0·0708	0·1	0·071	0·0708
(b) 8·027	8	8·0	8·03
(c) 90·39	90	90	90·4
(d) 73 270	70 000	73 000	73 300

Do not omit zeros in examples (c) and (d).

Rounding off a decimal to a given number of **decimal places** proceeds as follows:

1. If the last digit is greater than 5 the rounded off digit is increased by 1.
2. If the last digit is less than 5 the rounded off digit remains the same.
3. If the last digit is 5 there is no rule except that in statistics it is becoming more frequent to make the rounded-off digit even.

4·82678 is 4·8268 rounded-off to 4 decimal places
3·2632 is 3·263 rounded-off to 3 decimal places

Rounding off a decimal to a given number of **significant figures**. The decimal is rounded off as in the example above, several times if necessary until the desired number of significant figures is obtained.

A recurring decimal is one which cannot be written accurately no matter how many decimal places are given.

For example: $\frac{2}{3} = 0.6666\ldots$ which may be written as $0.\dot{3}$.

A recurring decimal can be rounded off in the same way as any other decimal, for example $\frac{2}{3} = 0.667$ to 3 significant figures. It is not correct to say $\frac{2}{3} = 0.666$.

The limits of accuracy are the range in which a given measurement can lie. For example, if a length is 9·2 cm to the nearest 0·1 cm the length can lie anywhere between 9·15 cm and 9·25 cm, i.e. 9.2 ± 0.05 cm. These are the limits of accuracy of the number 9·2.

Standard or scientific notation A number expressed in the form $A \times 10^n$, where A is a number between 1 and 10 and n is a positive or negative integer is written in standard form or scientific notation. This is particularly useful for expressing very large or very small numbers to avoid using large numbers of zeros.

Number	In standard form
327000	$3 \cdot 27 \times 10^5$
2400	$2 \cdot 4 \times 10^3$
0·0036	$3 \cdot 6 \times 10^{-3}$

Numbers less than 1 always have a negative power of 10.

Proportion

Direct proportion Two quantities m and n are directly proportional to each other if $m \propto n$, i.e. if $m = kn$ where k is a constant.

Inverse proportion Two quantities are inversely proportional if $m \propto 1/n$, i.e. $mn = k$ where k is a constant.

Ratios and percentages

A ratio compares two or more quantities. The ratio of two quantities a and b is $a:b$ if the result of dividing one by the other is $\frac{a}{b}$.

e.g.   125 cm and 55 cm are in the ratio $25:11$

A percentage, %, is a fraction with denominator 100.
To express one quantity as a percentage of another, express the one as a fraction of the other and then convert to a percentage.

To change a fraction to a percentage, multiply the fraction by 100.
$\frac{5}{8}$ becomes $\frac{5}{8} \times 100 = \frac{5}{2} \times 25 = \frac{125}{2} = 62 \cdot 5\%$

To change a decimal to a percentage move the decimal point two places to the right.
    0·423 becomes $42 \cdot 3\%$ 0·0546 becomes $5 \cdot 46\%$

Percentage changes
If a quantity is *increased* by 6% then
            initial value : increased value $= 100:106$

If a quantity is *decreased* by 6% then
            initial value : decreased value $= 100:94$

Logarithms

The logarithm of a number to base 10 is the power to which 10 must be raised to give the number.

Examples

$$10^2 = 100 \quad \therefore \quad \log 100 = 2$$
$$10^4 = 10000 \qquad \log 10000 = 4$$
$$10^{0.602} = 4 \qquad \log 4 = 0.602$$
$$10^{1.792} = 62 \qquad \log 62 = 1.792$$

The logarithm consists of a whole number before the decimal point, the characteristic, and a decimal part called the mantissa.

The characteristic of a logarithm is the whole number of a logarithm before the decimal point.

If the number is between 1 and 10 then the characteristic is zero.
If the number is greater than 10, the characteristic of the logarithm is positive.
If the number is less than 10, the characteristic is negative.

Examples

$$\text{characteristic of} \quad \log 7.24 = 0$$
$$\log 38.21 = 1$$
$$\log 0.421 = \bar{1} \text{ or } -1$$

The mantissa is the decimal part of the logarithm.

Example The numbers 1.25, 12.5, 125 all have the same mantissa.

$$\log 1.25 = 0.0969$$
$$\log 12.5 = 1.0969$$
$$\log 125 = 2.0969$$

Multiplication and division of numbers

Since $10^m \times 10^n = 10^{m+n}$ to multiply two numbers add their logarithms. This gives the logarithm of the product. To find the product use the antilogarithm tables.

Since $10^m \div 10^n = 10^{m-n}$ to divide two numbers subtract their logarithms. This gives the logarithm of the quotient. To find the quotient use the antilogarithms table.

Powers Since $(10^m)^n = 10^{mn}$, to find a power of a number multiply its logarithm by the power. Find the answer by using antilogarithm tables.

For example, to find $\sqrt[3]{46.4}$
Since $\sqrt[3]{46.4} = (46.4)^{1/3}$ find the log of 46.4 and divide by 3.

Profit and loss

Cost price In questions dealing with profit and loss the cost price is always taken as being 100 %.

e.g. If a person loses 15 % on selling a car then,

$$\text{Cost price} : \text{Selling price} = 100 : 85 \quad \text{i.e.} \quad \frac{\text{C.P.}}{\text{S.P.}} = \frac{100}{85}$$

$$\textbf{Percentage gain} = \frac{\text{actual gain}}{\text{initial value}} \times 100$$

$$\textbf{Percentage loss} = \frac{\text{actual loss}}{\text{initial value}} \times 100$$

$$\textbf{Percentage error} = \frac{\text{actual error}}{\text{correct value}} \times 100$$

Stocks and shares

Shares are the means by which an individual can invest his money, or business concerns can raise capital. They are generally issued in units of 5p, 10p, 25p, 50p or £1, known as the nominal value of the shares.

Stocks such as Government Securities and Local Loans are quoted in terms of £100 nominal value. Stock quoted as 6 % stock at 107 means that £100 stock (nominal value) would cost £107 cash. The income, which is based on the nominal value is 6 %.

The nominal value of a stock or share is the original price at which it is first issued.

The market value of a share or stock is the price at which it is quoted on the Stock Exchange.

The dividend is declared as a percentage of the nominal value of the share.

The yield is the income expressed as a percentage of the cash invested.

The rates on a house are expressed as so much in the £ on the rateable value.

For example, if the rates are 53p in the £ on a house of rateable value £103 then

$$\text{Rates} = 53 \times 103\text{p} = £54.59$$

Interest

The principal, P, is the sum of money loaned or borrowed.

The interest, I, is the money added to the principal by the lender for the privilege of borrowing the money.

The rate, R, usually expressed as a percentage, is the rate at which the interest is calculated.

The time, T, is the time over which the interest is calculated.

The amount repaid, A, = total repaid = principal + interest

$$A = P + I$$

Simple interest This is calculated annually on the sum (principal) borrowed.

The simple interest, I, paid on a principal, P, over a period of T years at $R\%$ per annum is given by

$$I = \frac{PRT}{100}$$

Principal, rate and time for simple interest may be expressed by rearrangement of the above formula

$$P = \frac{I \times 100}{RT}$$

$$R = \frac{I \times 100}{PT}$$

$$T = \frac{I \times 100}{PR}$$

Compound interest

In compound interest the interest is added to the principal at the end of each year so that the principal varies from year to year. The amount at the end of the year becomes the principal for the next year.

The amount (principal + interest) after T years is

$$A = P\left(1 + \frac{R}{100}\right)^T$$

The total interest = $A - P$

Areas and volumes

Triangle
Area of a triangle $\quad = \frac{1}{2}(\text{base} \times \text{height})$
$\qquad\qquad\qquad\qquad = \frac{1}{2}bh$

(any one of the sides may be taken as base)

Trapezium
Area of a trapezium $\quad = \left(\dfrac{\text{sum of parallel sides}}{2}\right) \times h$
$\qquad\qquad\qquad\qquad = \frac{1}{2}(a + b)h$

Parallelogram
Area of a parallelogram $\quad = \text{base} \times \text{height}$
$\qquad\qquad\qquad\qquad\quad = bh$

(any one of the sides may be taken as base)

Circle and sphere
Area of a circle $\qquad\qquad = \pi r^2$
Circumference of a circle $\quad = 2\pi r$
Volume of a sphere $\qquad\quad = \frac{4}{3}\pi r^3$
Curved surface area of sphere $\; = 4\pi r^2$

Curved surface area of a zone of a sphere, i.e. a part cut off by two parallel planes $= 2\pi rh$, where r is the radius of the sphere and h is the distance between the planes.

Cylinder of uniform cross-section
Volume of a cylinder $\qquad = \pi r^2 h$ where $r = $ radius,
$\qquad\qquad\qquad\qquad\qquad\qquad h = $ height
Curved surface area $\qquad = 2\pi rh$
of a cylinder
Total surface area $\qquad = 2\pi rh + 2\pi r^2$
of a cylinder

Cone
Volume of a cone $\qquad = \frac{1}{3}\pi r^2 h$ where $r = $ radius,
$\qquad\qquad\qquad\qquad\qquad\qquad h = $ vertical height
Curved surface area $\qquad = \pi rl$ where l is length of
of a cone $\qquad\qquad\qquad\qquad$ a slanted edge
Total area of a cone $\qquad = \pi rl + \pi r^2$

Prism
A prism is a solid with uniform cross-section. Cuboids and cylinders are prisms.

Volume of a prism $\qquad = \text{area of cross-section} \times h$
$\qquad\qquad\qquad\qquad\qquad\quad$ where $h = $ height

Pyramid

A pyramid is a solid formed by joining the vertices of a plane figure to a point not in its plane. Cones and tetrahedrons are examples of pyramids.

Volume of a pyramid $= \frac{1}{3}$ base area $\times$ height

Volume of a tetrahedron (base is triangular) $= \frac{1}{3}$ area of triangle $\times$ height

Volume between two surfaces

$=$ Volume of outer body $-$ volume of inner body

For example,

Volume of material in a spherical shell with outer radius R and inner radius $r = \frac{4}{3}\pi(R^3 - r^3)$

Volume of material in a circular pipe with outer radius R and inner radius r

$$= \pi R^2 h - \pi r^2 h$$
$$= \pi(R^2 - r^2)h$$
$$= \pi(R + r)(R - r)h$$

Algebra

Indices

An index is a power.

a^3 which equals $a \times a \times a$ is called 'a to the power 3'; a is called the base.

Laws of indices

When the bases are the same.

1. To multiply numbers add the indices.

$$x^m \times x^n = x^{m+n} \quad \text{e.g. } x^4 \times x^3 = x^7$$

2. To divide the numbers subtract the indices.

$$x^m \div x^n = x^{m-n} \quad \text{e.g. } x^7 \div x^2 = x^5$$

3. To raise a number to a power multiply the indices.

$$(x^m)^n = x^{mn} \quad \text{e.g. } (x^3)^2 = x^6$$

Note (i) Do not add or subtract indices when multiplying or dividing numbers with different bases.

$$\text{e.g. } x^4 \times y^3 = x^4 y^3 \qquad x^5 \div y^2 = x^5/y^2$$

(ii) $(4x)^2 = 16x^2$ (not $4x^2$)

Laws of algebra

Algebra is based on three laws—the Commutative Law, the Associative Law and the Distributive Law.

1. **The Commutative Law** The order in addition or the order in multiplication is immaterial, i.e.

$$a + b = b + a \qquad ab = ba$$

Subtraction and division are not commutative, i.e.

$$a - b \neq b - a \qquad a \div b \neq b \div a$$

2. **The Associative Law** In addition and in multiplication the terms may be bracketed in any way, without changing their value i.e.

$$(a + b) + c = a + (b + c) = a + b + c$$
$$(ab)c = a(bc)$$

Subtraction and division are not associative, i.e.

$$(a - b) + c \neq a - (b + c)$$
$$(a \div b) \div c \neq a \div (b \div c)$$

3. **The Distributive Law** A number outside a bracket multiplies each term inside the bracket, i.e.

$$a(b + c) = ab + ac$$
$$-a(b + c) = -ab - ac$$

Products (Brackets)
From the Distributive Law

1. $(a + b)(c + d) = a(c + d) + b(c + d) = ac + ad + bc + bd$

2. $-(a - b) = -a - -b = -a + b$

3. $(a + b)^2 = +a(a + b) + b(a + b)$
$\qquad\qquad = a^2 + ab + ba + b^2$
$\qquad\qquad = a^2 + 2ab + b^2$

4. $(a - b)^2 = a(a - b) - b(a - b)$
$\qquad\qquad = a^2 - ab - ba + b^2$
$\qquad\qquad = a^2 - 2ab + b^2$

5. $(a + b)(a - b) = a(a - b) + b(a - b)$
$\qquad\qquad\qquad = a^2 - ab + ba - b^2$
$\qquad\qquad\qquad = a^2 - b^2$

Factors

1. Obvious factor
First look for an obvious factor. Further factorization may then be possible, i.e.
$$5a^2 - 125b^2 = 5(a^2 - 25b^2) = 5(a + 5b)(a - 5b)$$

2. Difference of two squares
The fundamental identity is $x^2 - y^2 = (x + y)(x - y)$

Examples:
$$9a^2 - 25b^2 = (3a + 5b)(3a - 5b)$$
$$12a^2 - 27b^2 = 3(2a + 3b)(2a - 3b)$$
$$(3a + b)^2 - c^2 = (3a + b + c)(3a + b - c)$$

3. Trinomials
These are expressions containing three terms. To factorize $x^2 + bx + c$ two numbers must be found whose product equals c and whose sum equals b.
If b and c are positive then the numbers are positive.
If b and c are both negative then one number is positive, the other negative, and the larger number is negative.
If b is positive and c negative, one number is positive, the other negative, and the larger number is positive.
If b is negative and c positive then both numbers are negative.

Example:

To factorize $(x^2 - x - 12)$. Two numbers whose product is -12 and whose difference is -1 are -4 and 3. The factors are $(x - 4)(x + 3)$. Factorization is still a process of trial and error but the above guidelines are helpful.

4. Expressions containing four terms

Try grouping the expression into two pairs so that each pair has a common factor, e.g.

$$ax - ay - 2bx + 2by = a(x - y) - 2b(x - y)$$
$$= (x - y)(a - 2b)$$

If a common factor cannot be found this method fails; try the Factor theorem.

Factor theorem In general, if an expression equals 0 when $x = a$ then $(x - a)$ is a factor of that expression. Therefore a factor of an expression can be found by substituting values of $x = 1, 2, 3 \ldots$ into the expression until a value is found which makes the expression equal to 0.

5. Sum and difference of two cubes

The fundamental identities are:

$$x^3 + y^3 = (x + y)(x^2 - xy + y^2)$$
$$x^3 - y^3 = (x - y)(x^2 + xy + y^2)$$

Examples:

$$27x^3 + 8y^3 = (3x)^3 + (2y)^3 = (3x + 2y)(9x^2 - 6xy + 4y^2)$$
$$64A^3 - B^3 = (4A)^3 - B^3 = (4A - B)(16A^2 + 4AB + B^2)$$

Addition and subtraction of fractions in algebra is analogous to that in arithmetic.

Procedure:

1. Find the L.C.M. of the denominators.
2. Express each fraction as a fraction having this L.C.M. as denominator.
3. Simplify the numerator and cancel where possible.

Example 1:

$$\frac{x}{x - 1} - \frac{3}{x^2 + x - 2}$$

$$= \frac{x}{x - 1} - \frac{3}{(x - 1)(x + 2)}$$

$$= \frac{x(x+2) - 3}{(x-1)(x+2)} = \frac{x^2 + 2x - 3}{(x-1)(x+2)} = \frac{(x-1)(x+3)}{(x-1)(x+2)}$$

$$= \frac{x+3}{x+2}$$

Example 2.

To solve $\dfrac{2}{x^2 - 1} + \dfrac{1}{x^2 + 3x + 2}$

$$= \frac{2}{(x+1)(x-1)} + \frac{1}{(x+2)(x+1)}$$

$$= \frac{2(x+2) + (x-1)}{(x+1)(x-1)(x+2)} = \frac{3x+3}{(x+1)(x-1)(x+2)}$$

$$= \frac{3}{(x-1)(x+2)}$$

Solution of Equations

Simple equations

Procedure:
1. Find the lowest common multiple (L.C.M.) of the denominators.
2. Multiply throughout by this L.C.M.
3. Remove brackets.
4. Place all x terms on one side of the equation.
5. Solve for x.

Example:

To solve $\qquad \dfrac{3x+4}{2} + \dfrac{x-1}{3} = 2x + 1$

Multiply throughout by 6

$$3(3x+4) + 2(x-1) = 6(2x+1)$$

Remove brackets

$$9x + 12 + 2x - 2 = 12x + 6$$

Regroup: $\qquad 9x + 2x - 12x = 6 - 12 + 2$

$$-x = -4$$
$$x = 4$$

Check the answer by substituting this value of x into the original equation:

$$\frac{3 \times 4 + 4}{2} + \frac{4-1}{3} = 2 \times 4 + 1$$

$$8 \quad + \quad 1 \quad = 9$$

Simultaneous equations

A pair of equations such as $3x + 2y = 5$
$4x - y = 6$
are termed simultaneous. Each individual equation has an infinite number of solutions since for every different value of x a different value of y exists which satisfies the equation. However, there is, in general, only one pair of values of x and y which satisfy both equations at the same time, i.e. simultaneously.

Solution of simultaneous equations

To solve simultaneous equations it is necessary to find the values of x and y which satisfy both equations at the same time.
Procedure:
1. Collect all terms in x and y on the left-hand side.
2. Multiply each equation by factors which will make the coefficients of y equal.
3. Add or subtract to eliminate terms in y.
4. Solve the resulting equation for x.
5. Substitute the value of x in one of the original equations to find y.
Example:
To solve
$$2x = 5 - 3y$$
$$3x = 14 + 2y$$

Collect all x and y terms on left-hand side

	$2x + 3y = 5$	... (1)
	$3x - 2y = 14$	... (2)
Multiply (1) by 2	$4x + 6y = 10$	... (3)
Multiply (2) by 3	$9x - 6y = 42$	... (4)

Adding (3) and (4) to $\quad 13x \qquad = 52$
eliminate terms in $y \quad\quad x \qquad = 4$

Substitute in (1) $\quad 2 \times 4 + 3y = 5$
$$3y = 5 - 8$$
$$y = -1$$

(Check by substituting the values of x and y into (4)
$$9 \times 4 - 6 \times (-1) = 42$$

Quadratic equations A quadratic equation is of the form $ax^2 + bx + c = 0$ where a, b and c are constants. It contains a term x to the power two and no term in x has a greater power than 2. The equation has two solutions, known as '*roots*'.

Solution of quadratic equations

There are in general two methods:
1. By factors
2. By formula

73

1. By factors

This method is suitable when the equation factorizes. It is based on the assumption that if two quantities a and b are such that $ab = 0$ then either $a = 0$ or $b = 0$.

Example

To solve $$x^2 - x - 6 = 0$$

Factorize the left-hand side

$$(x - 3)(x + 2) = 0$$
$$x - 3 = 0 \quad \text{or} \quad x + 2 = 0$$
$$x = 3 \quad \text{or} \quad -2$$

2. By formula

When the quadratic equation does not factorize the roots of the equation $ax^2 + bx + c = 0$ may be found by using the formula

$$x = \frac{-b \pm \sqrt{b^2 - 4ac}}{2a}$$

Progressions

An arithmetic progression is a series in which each term is formed from the previous one by adding a constant. a is the first term and d is the constant term called the *common difference*.

The series is of the form: $a, a + d, a + 2d, a + 3d, \ldots (l - d), l$

$$n^{\text{th}} \text{ term} = a + (n - 1)d$$

$$\text{Sum of } n \text{ terms, } S, = \frac{n(a + l)}{2} = \frac{n}{2}\{2a + (n - 1)d\}$$

where l is the last term in the series.

A geometric progression is a series in which each term is formed from the previous one by multiplying by a constant factor, r. a is the first term and r is called the *common ratio*.

The series is of the form: $a, ar, ar^2, ar^3, \ldots$

$$n^{\text{th}} \text{ term} = ar^{n-1}$$

$$\text{Sum of } n \text{ terms, } S, = \frac{a(1 - r^n)}{1 - r}$$

If r is less than 1 then:

$$\text{Sum to infinity } S_\infty = \frac{a}{1 - r}$$

$$\text{and } r^n \to 0 \text{ as } n = \infty$$

Trigonometry

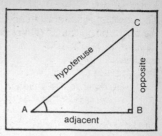

Figure 48.

Trigonometrical ratios

In figure 48 angle B is a right angle. The six trigonometrical ratios below are given with respect to angle A.

$$\sin A = \frac{\text{opposite}}{\text{hypotenuse}} = \frac{BC}{AC}$$

$$\cos A = \frac{\text{adjacent}}{\text{hypotenuse}} = \frac{AB}{AC}$$

$$\tan A = \frac{\text{opposite}}{\text{adjacent}} = \frac{BC}{AB}$$

$$\tan A = \frac{\sin A}{\cos A};$$

$$\sec A = \frac{1}{\cos A};$$

$$\operatorname{cosec} A = \frac{\text{hypotenuse}}{\text{opposite}} = \frac{AC}{BC}$$

$$\sec A = \frac{\text{hypotenuse}}{\text{adjacent}} = \frac{AC}{AB}$$

$$\cot A = \frac{\text{adjacent}}{\text{opposite}} = \frac{AB}{BC}$$

$$\operatorname{cosec} A = \frac{1}{\sin A};$$

$$\cot A = \frac{1}{\tan A}$$

The projection of a point B on to a plane is the distance AD where C is the foot of the perpendicular from B on to the plane (figure 49).

Angle of elevation
(figure 49)
If B is a point above the horizontal AC then angle BAC is called the angle of elevation of B from A.

Angle of depression
(figure 49)
If B is a point above the horizontal AC then angle DBA is called the angle of depression of A from B.

The angles of elevation and depression are alternate angles and are therefore equal.

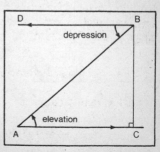

Figure 49.

The bearing of a point B from a point A is the direction in which one must travel in a straight line to get from A to B. It can be expressed either as an angle less than 90° measured E of W from the N-S line through B or as an angle measured clockwise from the N line through B. In figure 50 the bearing of B from A is 040° or N40°E. The bearing of A from B is 220° or S40°W.

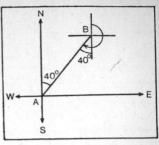

Figure 50

Complementary angles

$$\sin A = \cos(90° - A) \qquad \operatorname{cosec} A = \sec(90° - A)$$
$$\cos A = \sin(90° - A) \qquad \sec A = \operatorname{cosec}(90° - A)$$
$$\tan A = \cot(90° - A) \qquad \cot A = \tan(90° - A)$$

Examples: $\sin 20° = \cos 70°$; $\cos 45° = \sin 45°$; $\tan 30° = \cot 60°$

Supplementary angles

$$\sin A = \sin(180° - A) \qquad \operatorname{cosec} A = \operatorname{cosec}(180° - A)$$
$$\cos A = -\cos(180° - A) \qquad \sec A = -\sec(180° - A)$$
$$\tan A = -\tan(180° - A) \qquad \cot A = -\cot(180° - A)$$

Examples: $\sin 40° = \sin 140°$, $\cos 30° = -\cos 150°$.

45°, 45°, 90° triangle (figure 51)
This is a right angled isosceles triangle. If $AB = BC = 1$ unit then by Pythagoras' theorem $AC = \sqrt{2}$. From this triangle the trigonometrical ratios of the angle 45° can then be written in fraction form.

30°, 60°, 90° triangle
If $QR = 1$; $PR = 2$ then by Pythagoras' theorem $PQ = \sqrt{3}$. From this triangle the trigonometrical ratios of the angles 30° and 60° can be written in fraction form.

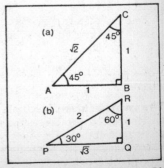

Figure 51

Trigonometrical ratios of 0°, 30°, 45°, 60°, and 90°

	0°	30°	45°	60°	90°
sin	0	$\dfrac{1}{2}$	$\dfrac{1}{\sqrt{2}}$	$\dfrac{\sqrt{3}}{2}$	1
cos	1	$\dfrac{\sqrt{3}}{2}$	$\dfrac{1}{\sqrt{2}}$	$\dfrac{1}{2}$	0
tan	0	$\dfrac{1}{\sqrt{3}}$	1	$\sqrt{3}$	∞

3-dimensional trigonometry

The angle between two lines which do not intersect is equal to the angle between two lines drawn parallel to the two original lines which do meet.

A plane is a surface such that a straight line joining any two points on the plane lies wholly on its surface.

The angle between a line and a plane is equal to the angle between the line and its projection on the plane.
For example, in figure 52 the line AC meets the plane $PQRS$ at point B. The perpendicular from A to the plane meets the plane at D. The angle between the line AC and the plane $PQRS$ is $A\hat{B}D$.

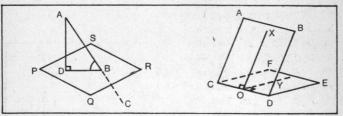

Figure 52

The angle between two planes which intersect is equal to the angle between two lines, one in each plane, which are drawn perpendicular to the line of intersection (common line) of the planes. For example, in figure 52 two lines are drawn from the points X and Y, which lie on the surfaces of the planes, perpendicular to the common line CD and meeting at a point O. $X\hat{O}Y$ is the angle between the planes.

Example of a 3-dimensional problem

Problems in 3-dimensional trigonometry can often be solved by considering the projection of the lines of the figure on to a plane or by considering a section of the figure made by some particular plane.

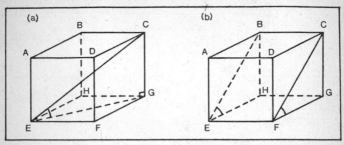

Figure 53

To calculate:
(i)   The angle between the line EC and the plane $EFGH$
(ii) The angle between the planes $BEFC$ and $EFGH$
Let $EF = 4$ cm; $CG = 3$ cm; $FG = 3$ cm

(i)   The projection of EC on to the plane $EFGH$ is EG

The angle required is $C\hat{E}G$

$$\tan C\hat{E}G = \frac{CG}{EG} = \frac{3}{\sqrt{4^2 + 3^2}} = \frac{3}{\sqrt{25}} = \frac{3}{5} = 0.6000$$

$\therefore \quad C\hat{E}G = 21°48'$

(ii) The angle between planes $BEFC$ and $EFGH$ is $B\hat{E}H$

$$\tan B\hat{E}H = \frac{BH}{EH} = \frac{3}{3} = 1$$

$\therefore \quad B\hat{E}H = 45°$

The Earth as a sphere

For the purpose of calculating distances on the earth's surface the earth is considered to be a sphere.

A great circle is formed by the intersection of the earth and a plane which passes through the centre of the earth.
The radius of the circle is equal to the radius of the earth.

A small circle is formed by the intersection of the earth and a plane which does not pass through the **centre of the earth**. The radius of a small circle is less than the radius of the earth.

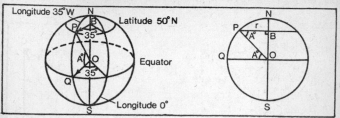

Figure 54

Longitude

1. **A meridian of longitude** is half of a great circle passing through the North and South poles. The equator and the meridian of longitude are perpendicular to each other.

Meridians of longitude are measured in degrees between 0° and 180° east or west of the line of longitude 0° which passes through Greenwich.

2. If the difference of longitude between two places on the equator is $x°$ the distance between the two places measured along the equator is $\dfrac{x°}{360°}(2\pi R)$, where R is the earth's radius.

3. If the difference of longitude between two places on a circle of latitude $\lambda°$ N is $x°$, the distance between the places measured along the circle of latitude is $\dfrac{x}{360°}(2\pi R \cos \lambda)$.

Latitude

1. **Circles of latitude** are small circles parallel to the equator with centres on the axis of the earth through the North and South poles. They are measured in degrees between 0° and 180° north or south of the equator.

2. The radius of a circle of latitude $A°$N is $R \cos A$ where R is the radius of the earth.

3. The circumference of a circle of latitude $A°$ North or South is the circumference of the earth $\times \cos A$.

A nautical mile is the distance on the equator subtending an angle of 1 minute at the centre of the earth.

A town of latitude 40°35′ S would be $(40 \times 60) + 35$ miles (nautical) south of the equator.

Graphs

Graphs of sin x, cos x and tan x

The sine and cosine curves are periodic curves with a period of 360° and an amplitude of 1 unit.

The cosine curve is the sine curve translated 90° along the x axis in the negative direction.

The tangent curve is a periodic curve with a period of 180°; it has no amplitude in the same way that the sine and cosine curves do.

x ranges from	$\sin x$ varies from	$\cos x$ varies from	$\tan x$ varies from
0°–90°	0 to 1	1 to 0	0 to $+\infty$
90°–180°	1 to 0	0 to −1	$-\infty$ to 0
180°–270°	0 to −1	−1 to 0	0 to $+\infty$
270°–360°	−1 to 0	0 to 1	$-\infty$ to 0

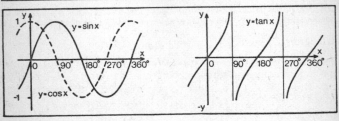

Figure 55

Graphs of 2 sin x and sin 2x

(i) $2 \sin x$. Doubling the ratio doubles the amplitude.

(ii) $\sin 2x$. Doubling the angle does not change the amplitude of the curve but the curve makes two oscillations every 360°.

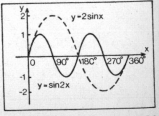

Figure 56

80

Identities, sine and cosine rule

Identities

1. $\tan x = \dfrac{\sin x}{\cos x}$

3. $\operatorname{cosec}^2 x - \cot^2 x = 1$

2. $\cos^2 x + \sin^2 x = 1$

4. $\sec^2 x - \tan^2 x = 1$

These are true for all values of x.

The sine rule

In any triangle $\dfrac{a}{\sin A} = \dfrac{b}{\sin B} = \dfrac{c}{\sin C}$

It is used to find the remaining sides in a triangle in which one side and two angles are known.

The cosine rule

In any triangle, $c^2 = a^2 + b^2 - 2ab \cos C$

or $\cos C = \dfrac{a^2 + b^2 - c^2}{2ab}$

It is used to find:
(i)   The third side of a triangle in which the other two sides and the angle between them are known.
(ii)   The angles of a triangle in which the three sides are given.

Area of a triangle

The area of a triangle is equal to half the product of two of its sides and the sine of the included angle.

Area of triangle $= \frac{1}{2}bc \sin A = \frac{1}{2}ac \sin B = \frac{1}{2}ab \sin C$.

Calculus

Calculus is a method of calculation which deals with such things as rates of change, areas under curves and volumes of curved solids. It provides a much more accurate method of determining, for example, gradients of curves than is possible graphically.

Differentiation

Differentiation is the process of finding the derived function which is equal to the gradient at any point on a curve.

Derived function (differential coefficient)
1. The derived function of $y = f(x)$ is the rate of change of y with respect to x. It is denoted $\dfrac{dy}{dx}$ or sometimes $f'(x)$.

2. $\dfrac{dy}{dx}$ is equal to the gradient of the curve $y = f(x)$ at the point (x, y).

3. If $y = x^n$ $\qquad \dfrac{dy}{dx} = nx^{n-1}$

n may be positive, negative, a whole number or a fraction.

4. If $y = ax^2 + bx + c$, where a, b and c are constants $\dfrac{dy}{dx} = 2ax + b$

Examples of differentiation

$f(x)$ or y	$f'(x)$ or $\dfrac{dy}{dx}$
4	0
$3x$	3
$2x^2$	$4x$
$2x^{-2}$	$-4x^{-3}$
$5x^{-1/3}$	$-\frac{5}{3}x^{-4/3}$

The differential of a sum = the sum of the differentials; if $y = ax^2 + bx + c$

$$\frac{dy}{dx} = \frac{d}{dx}(ax^2 + bx + c) = \frac{d(ax^2)}{dx} + \frac{d(bx)}{dx} + \frac{dc}{dx}$$

Gradient of a curve

The gradient of the curve $y = f(x)$ at the point (x, y) is determined by first differentiating y with respect to x and then inserting the values of x and y into the derived function

Maxima and Minima

A maximum point on a curve is a point at which the value of y is greater than at points immediately on either side of it. At a maximum point the gradient is zero, i.e. $\frac{dy}{dx} = 0$. The gradient $\frac{dy}{dx}$ changes from positive to negative through the point (figure 57).

A minimum point on a curve is a point at which the value of y is less than at points immediately on either side of it. At a minimum point the gradient is zero, i.e. $\frac{dy}{dx} = 0$. The gradient changes from negative to positive through the point (figure 57).

A point of inflection is a point on a curve at which the tangent to the curve is parallel to the x axis. The gradient $\frac{dy}{dx} = 0$ but it does not change sign through the point (figure 57).

A turning point is a point through which the gradient, $\frac{dy}{dx}$, changes sign. A turning point can be either a maximum or a minimum. A point of inflection is not a turning point.

A stationary point is a point at which $\frac{dy}{dx} = 0$. Maxima, minima and points of inflection are stationary points.

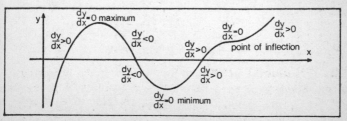

Figure 57

Determination of stationary points of the curve $y = f(x)$

Procedure:

1. Determine $\dfrac{dy}{dx}$ and equate it to zero.

2. Evaluate the values of x for which $\dfrac{dy}{dx} = 0$.

3. For each value of x, calculate the sign of $\dfrac{dy}{dx}$ for a value of x just to the left and for one just to the right of the point.

4. The type of stationary point may be obtained by reference to the following table.

Type of stationary point	Sign of $\dfrac{dy}{dx}$ just < stationary point	Sign of $\dfrac{dy}{dx}$ just > stationary point
maximum	+	−
minumum	−	+
point of inflection	or ±	±

Velocity

If v is the velocity of a body which moves in a straight line a distance s in time t then

$$v = \frac{ds}{dt}$$

Acceleration

If a is the acceleration of a body then

$$a = \frac{dv}{dt}$$

since $\dfrac{dv}{dt} = \dfrac{dv}{ds} \cdot \dfrac{ds}{dt}$ and $\dfrac{ds}{dt} = v$

$$a = v\frac{dv}{ds}$$

Integration

Integration can be considered to be the reverse of differentiation. Given the gradient at any point and the y intercept, integration is used to find the equation of the curve. By integrating between given limits the exact area under a curve can be found.

An indefinite integral is one which has no limits. It always contains an arbitrary constant. The value of the integral is given by:

$$\int x^n \, dx = \frac{x^{n+1}}{n+1} + C \text{ where } C \text{ is a constant.}$$

This is valid for all values of n except x^{-1}.

Examples of indefinite integrals

$f(x)$	$\int f(x) \, dx$
2	$2x + C$
$3x$	$\frac{3}{2}x^2 + C$
$2x^2$	$\frac{2}{3}x^3 + C$
$4x^{1/2}$	$\frac{8}{3}x^{3/2} + C$
$3x^{-1/3}$	$\frac{9}{2}x^{2/3} + C$

A definite integral has an upper and a lower limit.

$$\int_a^b x^n \, dx = \left[\frac{x^{n+1}}{n+1} \right]^b - \left[\frac{x^{n+1}}{n+1} \right]^a$$

Area under a curve

The area between the curve $y = f(x)$, the x axis and the lines $x = a$ and $x = b$ is given by

$$\int_a^b y \, dx$$

Area under velocity/time graph

The area under the velocity/time graph between t_1 and t_2 gives the distance travelled in time $(t_2 - t_1)$ i.e.

$$s_2 - s_1 = \int_{t_1}^{t_2} v \, dt$$

Area under acceleration/time graph

The area under the acceleration/time graph between t_1 and t_2 gives the velocity change in time $t_2 - t_1$

$$v_2 - v_1 = \int_{t_1}^{t_2} a \, dt$$

Statistics

Graphical representation

There are several different ways of illustrating statistics; which particular method is chosen depends on the nature of the data and the particular comparisons that are to be made.

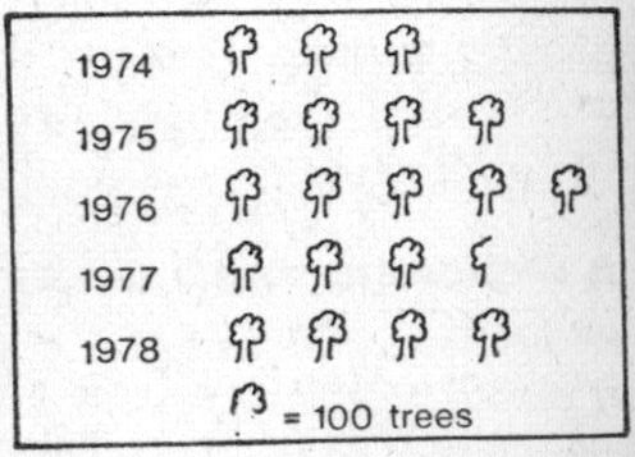

A pictogram is a pictorial way of representing statistical data. It uses symbols which look like the items they represent; each symbol denotes a certain quantity of the item. It is often used when representing statistical data to the public but it does not convey a particularly accurate picture especially when fractions of a symbol are used. Figure 59 shows a pictogram which represents the number of trees planted in a county during the last five years. Each symbol represents 100 trees.

1974	🌲 🌲 🌲
1975	🌲 🌲 🌲 🌲
1976	🌲 🌲 🌲 🌲 🌲
1977	🌲 🌲 🌲 🌲
1978	🌲 🌲 🌲 🌲

🌲 = 100 trees

Figure 58

A pie chart shows how a total is divided into its various parts. The total is represented by the full circle, and each part is represented by a sector of the circle. The area of the sector and hence the angle of the sector (since the two are proportional) represent the fraction the part is of the total. The table below shows the monetary value of the major exports of a country. The information is represented on the pie chart below.

Goods	£ million
coffee	103
cocoa beans	79
nuts	32
oil	28
timber	24
	266

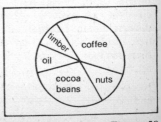

Figure 59

86

A frequency distribution is a table giving the frequency of different values of a variable. For example, the table opposite gives the frequency of the weights of cakes.

Weight (gm)	Frequency (secs)
20	6
21	2
22	10
23	9
24	5
25	10
26	4

A bar chart is a special type of histogram. Since all the bars are the same width, the height of a bar is proportional to the quantity graphed. The vertical axis is the frequency axis (see figure 60).

A frequency polygon is obtained by joining the midpoints of the top of each bar in the bar chart. The lines between these points have no particular significance but make it easier to see the rise and fall in frequency of the quantity plotted (figure 60).

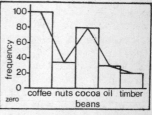

Figure 60

A histogram (frequency chart) is a graphical way of representing a frequency distribution. The bars may be of varying widths, representing different ranges of the quantity plotted on the horizontal axis. The vertical axis represents the frequency/range, since the frequency of the quantity depends both on the height and the width of the bar.

Frequency = area of bar = height × width

If the width of the bar is constant and equal to 1 then the height of the bar equals the frequency (the histogram is then really a bar chart). In figure 61:

No. of people aged between 25 and 30 = 4 × 5 = 20

No. of people aged between 60 and 80 = 0·6 × 20 = 12.

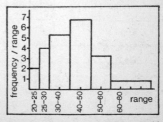

Figure 61

Class distribution When the spread of values is very large it is often unnecessary to consider the frequency of each individual value of the variable. Instead the data may be grouped into classes, each class representing a range of values. The class interval represents the difference between the upper and lower end of the range. For example, the table below gives the class distribution for the marks obtained in an examination with a maximum mark of 40.

1–5	6–10	11–15	16–20	21–25	26–30	31–35	36–40
6	10	14	29	35	31	22	11

Averages

The mode is the class which has the highest frequency.

The modal class is the highest frequency of a class distribution. For example, in the table above the modal class is 21–25 marks.

The mean (arithmetic mean) $= \dfrac{\text{sum of the items}}{\text{number of items}}$

The mean of the numbers $x_1, x_2, x_3, \ldots x_n = \dfrac{1}{n}(x_1 + x_2 + \cdots x_n)$.

For a small number of items the above formula is useful.

(i) **Mean of a frequency distribution**

$$= \frac{\text{sum of (items} \times \text{frequency)}}{\text{sum of the frequency}} = \frac{\sum xf}{\sum f}$$

For example, the mean of the frequency distribution on p. 87.

$$= \frac{(20 \times 6) + (21 \times 2) + (22 \times 10) + (23 \times 9) + (24 \times 5) + (25 \times 10) + (26 \times 4)}{6 + 2 + 10 + 9 + 5 + 10 + 4}$$

$$= \frac{1063}{46}$$

$\therefore$ the mean $= 23.1$

(ii) **Mean of a class distribution** It would be possible to find the mean of a large number of items by finding the sum of the items and dividing by the number of items, but this would be tedious and inefficient. An alternative method is to group the data and to take the mode as a reasonable estimate of the mean and then find the correction required to the mode to find the true mean.

Example. To find the mean of the marks obtained by pupils in an examination for which the maximum mark is 30.

Procedure:
1. Group the data—this immediately reduces the number of items.
2. Determine the number of pupils in each group.
3. Find the middle mark of each group (mid-value).
4. For each group find the difference between the mid-value and the modal mark, called x.

5. Then mean of x, $\bar{x} = \dfrac{\sum xf}{\sum f}$ which represents the difference between the mode and the true mean. Hence true mean $\bar{X} = \text{mode} + \bar{x}$

Mark range	No. of pupils (frequency) f	Middle mark (mid-value) x	Difference between mid-value and modal mark x	fx
1–5	4	3	− 15	− 60
6–10	7	8	− 10	− 70
11–15	11	13	− 5	− 55
16–20	36	18	0	0
21–25	14	23	+ 5	+ 70
26–30	8	28	+ 10	+ 80
	80			

Then mean of $x = \dfrac{\sum xf}{\sum f} = \dfrac{-35}{80} = -0.44$

$\therefore$ true mean $\bar{X} = \text{mode} + \bar{x} = 18 + -0.44 = 17.56$

The median of a set of items arranged in order of magnitude (ranked) is the value of the middle item.

If there are n items the rank of the median is $\dfrac{n+1}{2}$. The value of this item is the median.

If n is even then there is no middle item and the median is taken as the average (mean) of the two middle items.

For example, to find
(i) the median of the numbers 8, 9, 11, 12, 14, 17, 19
The rank of the median $= \frac{1}{2}(7 + 1) = 4$
the median is the value of the 4th item $= 12$
(ii) the median of the numbers 22, 24, 27, 31, 35, 37
The rank of the median $= \frac{1}{2}(6 + 1) = \frac{7}{2} = 3\frac{1}{2}$
the median is the mean of the 3rd and 4th item $= \frac{1}{2}(27 + 31) = 29$

Median of a frequency distribution To find the median of the frequency distribution in the table on p. 90 group the numbers in ascending order in the table and add the frequencies from the top.

i.e. $6 + 2 = 8, 6 + 2 + 10 = 18, 6 + 2 + 10 + 9 = 27.$

The 23rd term (since the rank of the median is 23) lies in the class of nine 23's

∴   the median is 23 grams.

Median of a class distribution. Construct a cumulative frequency distribution. Draw a horizontal line passing through the vertical axis at a value equal to the rank of the median. Read off the value on the horizontal scale corresponding to the point of intersection of the horizontal line and the curve.

Cumulative frequency distribution is a table formed from a frequency distribution by adding in each frequency in succession.

Quantiles

Quantiles show how a distribution is spread on either side of the median. Quantiles which divide a ranked distribution into 4 equal parts are called quartiles; if into 6 equal parts sextiles; if into 100 equal parts **percentiles**.

The lower quartile bisects the lower half of a set of items.

The lower quartile rank of a set of N items $= \dfrac{N+1}{4}$

The upper quartile bisects the upper half of a set of items.

The upper quartile rank of a set of N items $= 3\dfrac{(N+1)}{4}$

Interquartile range is the difference between the lower and upper quartiles.
It is a useful measure of spread since it measures the dispersion of the numbers in the middle.

The range gives the difference between the largest and smallest values of the data.
It can be misleading as a measure of spread since it includes exceptional cases which differ in value greatly from the average.

Probability

Probability =

The number of ways in which a particular event can occur.
_____
The total number of events

If p = the probability of an event occurring
q = the probability of an event not occurring

then $p + q = 1$ where p, q are fractions between 0 and 1.

Compound probability If two independent events have probabilities p and q, the probability that they both take place is pq.

Total probability If two events with probabilities p and q are mutually exclusive, i.e. one event has no effect on the other, then the probability that they both take place is $p + q$.

A tree diagram is a systematic way of writing down all the possibilities. It is very useful for problems which seem to be more complicated.

For example: A bag contains 4 black balls and 3 white balls. If two balls are drawn find the probability that (i) both are white (ii) one is white and one black.

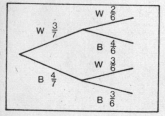

Note that after the first ball is drawn, six balls remain in the bag.

Figure 62

To find the answer trace along the appropriate branch
(i) Probability that both are white is $\frac{3}{7} \times \frac{2}{6} = \frac{1}{7}$
(ii) Probability of white then black $\frac{3}{7} \times \frac{4}{6} = \frac{2}{7}$
Probability of black then white $\frac{4}{7} \times \frac{3}{6} = \frac{2}{7}$
Total probability of a white and a black $\frac{2}{7} + \frac{2}{7} = \frac{4}{7}$

Metric Units

Length	kilometre	km	$1\,km = 1\,000\,m$
	metre	m	$1\,m = 100\,cm$
	centimetre	cm	$1\,cm = 10\,mm$

Area	kilometre squared	km^2	$1\,km^2 = 10^6\,m^2$
	metre squared	m^2	$1\,m^2 = 10^4\,cm^2$
	centimetre squared	cm^2	$1\,cm^2 = 10^2\,mm^2$
			$(1\,hectare = 10^4\,m^2)$

Volume	kilometre cubed	km^3	$1\,km^3 = 10^9\,m^3$
	metre cubed	m^3	$1\,m^3 = 10^6\,cm^3$
	centimetre cubed	cm^3	$1\,cm^3 = 10^3\,mm^3$

Mass	tonne (metric ton)		$1\,tonne = 1\,000\,kg$
	kilogram	kg	$1\,kg = 1\,000\,g$
	gram	g	$1\,g = 1\,000\,mg$

Capacity	litre	l	$1\,l = 1\,000\,ml$
			$= 1\,000\,cm^3$
	millilitre	ml	$1\,ml = 1\,cm^3$

Formulae: a summary

Triangles

Pythagoras' theorem
$$a^2 = b^2 + c^2$$

acute-angled $a^2 = b^2 + c^2 - 2bc \cos A$
obtuse-angled
$$a^2 = b^2 + c^2 + 2bc \cos A$$
any triangle $b^2 + c^2 = 2a^2 + 2m^2$

Lamis theorem
$$\frac{P}{\sin \alpha} = \frac{Q}{\sin \beta} = \frac{R}{\sin \gamma}$$

Logarithms

$$\log mn = \log m + \log n$$
$$\log \frac{m}{n} = \log m - \log n$$
$$\log m^2 = n \log m$$

Simple interest, $I = \dfrac{PRT}{100}$

Compound interest
Amount, $A = P(1 + R)^T$

Indices

$$x^m \times x^n = x^{m+n}$$
$$x^m \div x^n = x^{m-n}$$
$$(x^m)^n = x^{mn}$$

Formula solution of quadratic equation

$$x = \frac{-b \pm \sqrt{b^2 - 4ac}}{2a}$$

Arithmetic progression

nth term $= a + (n - 1)d$

Sum of n terms, $S = \dfrac{n(a + l)d}{2}$

Geometric progression

nth term $= ar^{n-1}$

Sum of n terms, $S = \dfrac{a(1 - r^n)}{1 - r}$

Sum to infinity, $S_\infty = \dfrac{a}{1 - r}$

Trigonometric ratios

$$\sin A = \frac{\text{opp.}}{\text{hypot.}}$$

$$\csc A = \frac{\text{hypot.}}{\text{opp.}}$$

$$\cos A = \frac{\text{adj.}}{\text{hypot.}}$$

$$\sec A = \frac{\text{hypot.}}{\text{adj.}}$$

$$\tan A = \frac{\text{opp.}}{\text{adj.}}$$

$$\cot A = \frac{\text{adj.}}{\text{opp.}}$$

$$\sin A = \csc A$$
$$\cos A = \sec A$$

$$\tan A = \frac{\sin A}{\cos A}$$

$$\tan A = \frac{1}{\cot A}$$

Identities

$$\cos^2 x + \sin^2 x = 1$$
$$\csc^2 x - \cot^2 x = 1$$
$$\sec^2 x - \tan^2 x = 1$$

Sine rule

$$\frac{a}{\sin A} = \frac{b}{\sin B} = \frac{c}{\sin C}$$

Index

Other study aids in the  series

KEY FACTS CARDS

Latin
Julius Caesar
New Testament
German
Macbeth
Geography Regional
English Comprehension
English Language
Economics
Elementary Mathematics
Algebra
Modern Mathematics

English History (1815–1939)
Chemistry
Physics
Biology
Geometry
Geography
French
Arithmetic &
    Trigonometry
General Science
Additional Mathematics
Technical Drawing

KEY FACTS COURSE COMPANIONS

Economics
Modern Mathematics
Algebra
Geometry
Arithmetic &
    Trigonometry
Additional Mathematics

Geography
French
Physics
Chemistry
English
Biology

KEY FACTS A-LEVEL BOOKS

Chemistry
Biology

Pure Mathematics
Physics

KEY FACTS PASSBOOKS

Modern Mathematics
English History
    (1815–1939)
Biology
Chemistry

Physics
Geography
French
English

KEY FACTS MODEL ANSWERS

Modern Mathematics
English History
    (1815–1939)
Biology
Chemistry

Physics
Geography
French
English

KEY FACTS REFERENCE LIBRARY

O-Level Traditional
    & Modern Mathematics

O-Level Biology
O-Level Physics
O-Level Chemistry